THE ILLUSTRATORS 1865-2019

No.	Price	No.	Price	No.	Price	No.	Price	No.	Price
1	2250	35	2750	69	350	103	850	137	2450
2	1750	36	1750	70	350	104	950	138	2750
3	750	37	1450	71	7500	105	5500	139	450
4	1450	38	2450	72	5500	106	2750	140	1650
5	1750	39	1750	73	4750	107	2750	141	1750
6	3500	40	1450	74	1750	108	3750	142	850
7	450	41	1250	75	950	109	7500	143	3750
8	650	42	850	76	950	110	4750	144	4500
9	850	43	1250	77	950	111	5500	145	ON LOAN
10	65000	44	950	78	850	112	3500	146	ON LOAN
11	1250	45	950	79	1250	113	2750	147	4500
12	3500	46	950	80	950	114	3250	148	5500
13	2750	47	1450	81	950	115	650	149	3750
14	1450	48	1750	82	1250	116	2250	150	7500
15	1450	49	6500	83	1450	117	950	151	7500
16	1750	50	75000	84	6500	118	950	152	9500
17	1750	51	1850	85	4500	119	750	153	2750
18	450	52	1650	86	2500	120	1750	154	8500
19	450	53	2250	87	ON LOAN	121	3750	155	1750
20	1750	54	1750	88	4750	122	2750	156	2750
21	550	55	1450	89	2750	123	3500	157	2750
22	6500	56	6500	90	3500	124	1750	158	2750
23	3750	57	4500	91	4750	125	3500	159	2750
24	6500	58	6500	92	5500	126	750	160	3750
25	2750	59	3500	93	3500	127	850	161	2750
26	4500	60	2250	94	2500	128	1250	162	2750
27	1750	61	650	95	2250	129	2450	163	450
28	2750	62	6500	96	3750	130	1750	164	550
29	2250	63	7500	97	2750	131	2750	165	850
30	6500	64	350	98	2750	132	3750	166	650
31	4500	65	350	99	4500	133	1750	167	550
32	3500	66	350	100	3250	134	1750	168	1250
33	3500	67	350	101	1450	135	ON LOAN	169	950
34	2250	68	350	102	1250	136	1750	170	1250

171	1750	203	2250	235	1750	267	650
172	1450	204	2250	236	1250	268	350
173	650	205	3750	237	2750	269	350
174	650	206	2250	238	2750	270	350
175	650	207	2250	239	2250	271	350
176	650	208	3750	240	950	272	350
177	1750	209	3500	241	1250	273	350
178	2250	210	3500	242	1750	274	350
179	1450	211	3750	243	1250	275	350
180	550	212	4250	244	850	276	350
181	650	213	4500	245	750	277	350
182	650	214	4750	246	550	278	1250
183	12500	215	2750	247	650	279	1450
184	14500	216	2250	248	750	280	1250
185	4500	217	1750	249	650	281	950
186	1750	218	1450	250	550	282	1450
187	1450	219	550	251	450		
188	750	220	1250	252	450		
189	850	221	1450	253	450		
190	1450	222	1750	254	450		
191	2750	223	3500	255	1450		
192	2750	224	650	256	1450		
193	1250	225	750	257	1450		
194	1250	226	850	258	1450		
195	4250	227	1250	259	1750		
196	1450	228	950	260	1750		
197	1750	229	1450	261	1250		
198	1450	230	2250	262	750		
199	2250	231	950	263	750		
200	2250	232	2250	264	850		
201	2250	233	1450	265	850		
202	1750	234	850	266	750		

www.chrisbeetles.com

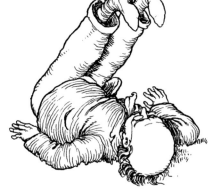

Copyright © Chris Beetles Ltd 2019
8 & 10 Ryder Street
St James's
London SW1Y 6QB
020 7839 7551
gallery@chrisbeetles.com
www.chrisbeetles.com

ISBN 978-1-905738-93-9

Cataloguing in publication data is available
from the British Library

Researched and written by David Wootton
Edited by Alexander Beetles, Fiona Nickerson,
Pascale Oakley and David Wootton

Design by Fiona Nickerson and
Pascale Oakley
Photography by Julian Huxley-Parlour
Reproduction by www.cast2create.com
Colour separation and printing by
Geoff Neal Litho Limited

For John Burningham
(1936-2019)
The Best of the Best.

Front cover:
Arthur Rackham
*They were ruled by an old Squaw spirit
who hung up the new moons in the skies
and cut up the old ones into stars* [10]

Front endpaper:
Rowland Emett
Well Met by Lamp Light [148]

This page:
William John Hennessy
The Swallows (detail) [24]

Back endpaper:
Amanda Hall
Leonora's World [239]

Back cover:
Michael Foreman
*Down they went, through the snow
towards the bright flashing lights of
the city* [213]

PETER CROSS
Peter Cross (born 1951)

From 1975, Peter Cross began to emerge as an illustrator of great originality, making his name with
books that continue to delight children and adults alike. Unwilling to restrict his fertile imagination to
two dimensions, he also created a series of eccentric cabinets of curiosities. Such richness and variety
were then directed towards advertising and, in particular, to delightful work for the company
Wine Rack. Cross's dry, yet charming visual-verbal wit has reached a wide international public through
designs for greetings cards, first for Gordon Fraser (Hallmark 1995-2000) and then for The Great
British Card Company.

For a biography of Peter Cross, please refer to *The Illustrators*, 2018, Page 150.

TITLE PAGE
Hooray!
Signed with initials
Pen ink and watercolour
3 ½ x 5 inches

THE ILLUSTRATORS

THE BRITISH ART OF ILLUSTRATION
1865-2019

CHRIS BEETLES GALLERY

8 & 10 Ryder Street, St James's, London SW1Y 6QB
020 7839 7551   gallery@chrisbeetles.com
www.chrisbeetles.com

JOHN TENNIEL
Sir John Tenniel, RI (1820-1914)

While best remembered as the illustrator of Lewis Carroll's Alice books, John Tenniel contributed greatly to the look of *Punch* during the later nineteenth century. Beautifully drawn and highly allusive, his political cartoons remain startling in presenting fantastic imagery with classical polish.

For a biography of John Tenniel, please refer to *The Illustrators*, 2009, Page 24. For an essay on the critical reception of Tenniel's work, see *The Illustrators*, 1996, Pages 127-131.

His work is represented in the collections of the British Museum and the V&A.

Further reading
L Perry Curtis Jnr, 'Tenniel, Sir John (1820-1914)', H C G Matthew and Brian Harrison (eds), *Oxford Dictionary of National Biography*, Oxford University Press, 2004, Vol 54, Pages 131-134; Rodney Engen, *Sir John Tenniel: Alice's White Knight*, London: Scolar Press, 1991; Roger Simpson, *Sir John Tenniel: Aspects of His Work*, Cranbury: Associated University Presses, 1994

SIR JOHN TENNIEL.

Paradise and the Peri
The present cartoon celebrated the election of Benjamin Disraeli as Conservative Prime Minister on 20 February 1874. Though it marked the beginning of a second ministry that lasted until 1880, it was the first time that he had gained his position as the result of a general election. On the previous occasion, in 1868, he had taken over from Lord Derby while the Conservatives were in power, and then lost the general election to William Gladstone later the same year. This loss was mainly due to his introduction of the 1867 Reform Act, which was intended to help the Conservatives by doubling the number of adult males eligible to vote, but had the opposite effect.

The title of the cartoon, *Paradise and the Peri*, and the accompanying quotation allude to Thomas Moore's Oriental romance, *Lalla Rookh* (1817). Tenniel illustrated an edition of the poem, published by Longman in 1861, and based Disraeli's pose in the cartoon on a particular image in that volume. The poem was highly popular throughout the nineteenth century, and cited by Disraeli himself in some of his novels, including *The Young Duke* (1831) and *Consingsby* (1844). It also inspired a number of works of music. The most famous of these is the oratorio by the German composer, Robert Schumann, which was composed in 1843 and received its English premiere in 1856. However, at least two native composers also wrote responses: Sterndale Bennett producing a 'Fantasia-Overture' (1862) and John Francis Barnett a cantata (1870). All three received regular performances during the early 1870s.

Paradise and the Peri concerns a 'peri', a winged spirit of Persian mythology, who is trying to regain entrance to Heaven by bringing it a cherishable gift. The peri is admitted when it offers a tear from the cheek of a repentant old sinner who has seen a child praying. In the verses that accompany Tenniel's cartoon, Disraeli enters 'Downing Street Heaven' by offering 'Ballot, and Bible, and Beer!'

Tenniel's cartoon was not the first to represent Disraeli as a peri, or to link him to the precise quotation from Thomas Moore, 'Joy, joy for ever! My task is done'. Another appeared seven years earlier, in the issue of *Fun* for 31 August 1867. Ironically, it was a response to the passing of the 1867 Reform Act.

1 PARADISE AND THE PERI
'JOY, JOY FOR EVER! MY TASK IS DONE –
THE GATES ARE PASSED, AND HEAVEN IS WON!'
LALLA ROOKH
Signed with monogram and dated 1874
Inscribed with title on original mount
Pencil, 8 ¼ x 6 ¼ inches
Illustrated: *Punch*, 28 February 1874, Page 89

2 THE POLITICAL 'WALL-FLOWER'!
MISS BRIGHT: 'NOBODY ASKS ME; — AND IF THEY DID I SHOULD CERTAINLY DECLINE'
Signed with monogram and dated 1865
Inscribed with title and 'Punch', and dated 'Nov 25 1865' on original mount
Pencil
6 ¼ x 8 ¼ inches
Illustrated: *Punch*, 25 November 1865, Page 209

The Political 'Wall-Flower'!

In October 1865, Lord John Russell became Liberal Prime Minister for the second time, following the death of Lord Palmerston. Tenniel's cartoon presents Russell's attempts to build his ministry as if he were courting ladies at a social event. He can be seen talking to 'Miss Göschen' in the background of the image and, in the November, George Goschen would become Vice-President of the Board of Trade and Paymaster-General. The verses that accompany the cartoon in *Punch* also mention William Edward Forster, who would become Under-Secretary of State for the Colonies in the same month, James Stansfeld, who would become Under-Secretary of State for India in February 1866.

However, the image is dominated by 'Miss Bright', a caricature of John Bright, the Liberal MP for Birmingham, who, sitting alone in a separate room, is a 'political "wall-flower"'. Though one of the greatest orators of

the age, who was key to the success of the Liberal Party, he had often disagreed with its leading figures, including Russell, on significant issues. For instance, in 1848, when Russell brought forward the anti-Catholic 'Ecclesiastical Titles Bill', Bright opposed it as 'a little, paltry, miserable measure', and foretold its failure. Similarly, in 1854, Russell defended Britain's involvement in the Crimean War, while Bright was against it. So the caption to the cartoon suggests that Russell is unlikely to invite Bright to join his ministry and that, even if he does, he would decline. In the event, he toured the country and spoke in support of parliamentary reform, during Russell's short-lived ministry, which lasted only until 1866. He would later serve in William Gladstone's cabinets in various positions between 1868 and 1882.

Silencing the Trumpet (after Aesop)

When William Gladstone became Liberal Prime Minister for the first time in 1868, he stated that, 'my mission is to pacify Ireland', and planned to deal with the three main grievances of the Irish, namely church, land and education. Almost immediately, in 1869, parliament took decisive action regarding the first of these by passing the Irish Church Act, which had the intention of disestablishing the (Anglican) Church of Ireland. Gladstone then turned his attention to the second issue, and put forward a bill that would give greater rights to tenants, which was passed as the Landlord and Tenant (Ireland) Act in 1870. (However, he would not progress with education until later in the decade.)

While this legislation was going through parliament, public disorder actually increased in Ireland, and Gladstone was forced, against his better nature, to bring in a 'Coercion Act' to quell such outbreaks by force. Passed in 1871 as the Protection of Life and Property in Certain Parts of Ireland Act, it was also known as the Westmeath Act; for County Westmeath, to the west of Dublin, was a particular hotbed of Ribbonism, a popular movement of poor Catholics rising against Protestant landlords and their agents.

During these years, *Punch* published several cartoons on the subject of disorder in Ireland, including John Tenniel's controversial *The Irish 'Tempest'*, which appeared on 19 March 1870. Employing characters from Shakespeare's *The Tempest*, this showed Gladstone as Prospero protecting Ireland, in the shape of his daughter Miranda, from the Irish nationalist 'Rory of the Hills' who looks like the monstrous Caliban and speaks his line: 'This Ireland's mine, by Sycorax my mother, which thou tak'st from me'.

Three weeks later, on 9 April 1870, the present cartoon drew attention to the fact that the Coercion Act would deal not only with the disorder itself but also with those who inflame it. Taking as his text, Aesop's moral, 'He who incites to strife is worse than he who takes part in it', Tenniel shows Gladstone as a constable seizing the trumpet from an Irish newspaper editor, who embodies the 'seditious press'.

3 SILENCING THE TRUMPET (AFTER AESOP)
FENIAN TRUMPETER: 'SPARE ME, GOOD SIR, I BESEECH YOU. I HAVE NO ARMS BUT THIS TRUMPET ONLY!'
CONSTABLE: 'NO, YOU VAGABONE! WITHOUT THE SPIRIT TO FIGHT YOURSELF, YOU STIR UP OTHERS TO WAR AND BLOODSHED.'
MORAL — HE WHO INCITES TO STRIFE IS WORSE THAN HE WHO TAKES PART IN IT
Signed with monogram
Pencil
7 ¾ x 6 inches
Illustrated: *Punch*, 9 April 1870, Page 141

GEORGE DU MAURIER
George Louis Palmella Busson Du Maurier (1834-1896)

Equally talented as artist and writer, George Du Maurier developed a cartoon format for *Punch* that balanced text and image in order to record and satirise the fashions and foibles of society.

For a biography of George Du Maurier, please refer to *The Illustrators*, 2009, Page 30.

His work is represented in numerous public collections, including the British Museum and the V&A.

Further reading

Leonée Ormond, 'Du Maurier, George Louis Palmella Busson (1834-1896)', H C G Matthew and Brian Harrison (eds), *Oxford Dictionary of National Biography*, Oxford University Press, 2004, Vol 17, Pages 177-180; Leonée Ormond, *George Du Maurier*, London: Routledge & Kegan Paul, 1969; Leonée Ormond, 'Du Maurier, George (Louis Palmella Busson) (*b* Paris, 6 March 1834; *d* London, 8 Oct 1896)', in Jane Turner (ed), *The Dictionary of Art*, London: Macmillan, 1996, Vol 9, Page 384

4 COLD COMFORT!

AUNT PHILLIDA: 'THE LAST TIME I WENT TO A GROWN-UP FANCY BALL, I WENT AS A WASP. THAT WAS ONLY TEN YEARS AGO. I DON'T SUPPOSE I SHALL EVER AGAIN GO TO A FANCY BALL AS A WASP!' [SIGHS DEEPLY]
MARY: 'HARDLY AS A WASP, AUNT PHILLIDA. BUT YOU'D LOOK VERY SPLENDID AS A BUMBLE-BEE!'
Signed
Inscribed with title and 'Punch May 11th 1895' on reverse
Pen and ink
7 x 11 inches
Illustrated: *Punch*, 11 May 1895, Page 222

5 INTERNATIONAL AMENITIES

COUNT PETER VON STRUBEL (JUST ARRIVED IN ENGLAND IN TIME FOR HER GRACE'S CONCERT): 'ACH! TOTCHESS! HOW IZ IT ZAT IN ENKLAND YOUR LATIES ZOH PEAUDIFUL AND YOUR CHENDLEMEN ARE ZOH OCKLY?'

HER GRACE: 'TONIGHT ALL THE LADIES ARE ENGLISH, COUNT, AND THE GENTLEMEN ARE MOSTLY FOREIGN – AS IT HAPPENS!'

Signed

Signed, inscribed with title and dated '½ p Punch great care' and dated 'Hampstead Aug 92' below mount

Pen and ink

7 x 11 ¾ inches

Illustrated: *Punch*, 20 August 1892, Page 78

PHIL MAY
Philip William May, RI RP NEAC (1864-1903)

Sometimes referred to as the 'grandfather of British illustration', Phil May was one of the most influential black-and-white artists of his generation. Earthy, street-wise, and redolent of the music hall, his work is the antithesis of Aubrey Beardsley.

For a biography of Phil May, please refer to *The Illustrators*, 2017, page 36.

His work is represented in numerous public collections, including the British Museum, the National Portrait Gallery, Tate and the V&A; Leeds Art Gallery; and the Fine Arts Museums of San Francisco and the National Library of Australia (Canberra).

Further reading

David Cuppleditch, *Phil May. The Artist and His Wit*, London: Fortune Press, 1981; Simon Houfe, 'May, Philip William [Phil] (1864-1903)', H C G Matthew and Brian Harrison (eds), *Oxford Dictionary of National Biography*, Oxford University Press, 2004, Vol 37, Pages 556-558; 'Simon Houfe, *Phil May. His Life and Work, 1864-1903*, Aldershot: Ashgate, 2002; James Thorpe, *Phil May*, London: Art and Technics, 1948

6 A PORTRAIT OF A CALCULATING GENTLEMAN (NOT AT ALL A BAD LOOKING CHAP) WHO HAS SOLVED THE PROBLEM AS TO WHETHER WE ARE IN THE NINETEENTH OR TWENTIETH CENTURY
Signed and dated 1900
Pen and ink
9 x 7 ¼ inches
Illustrated: *Punch*, 10 January 1900, Page 32
Exhibited: 'Some British Illustrators, Watercolours and Drawings from 1840', Fine Art Society, London, June 1965, No 44

7 A JUG; A MUG
Pen and ink, 2 ½ x 2 ¼ inches
Illustrated: *Phil May's Illustrated Annual*, Winter Number 1901-1902,
London: W Thacker & Co, 1901, Page 94; *Phil May's Illustrated Annual*,
Summer Number 1902, London: W Thacker & Co, 1902, Page 16

8 THE CAVALIER
Pen and ink, 3 ½ x 3 ¼ inches
Illustrated: *Phil May's Illustrated Annual*, Winter Number 1901-1902,
London: W Thacker & Co, 1901, Page 67

9 MOSAIC ORNAMENTS
Signed, inscribed with title and dated 1901
Pen and ink, 6 ¼ x 5 inches
Illustrated: *Phil May's Illustrated Annual*, Winter Number 1903-1904,
London: W Thacker & Co, 1903, Page 65

ARTHUR RACKHAM
Arthur Rackham, VPRWS (1867-1939)

If the major gift book illustrators were to divide the world between them, Arthur Rackham would claim the northern lands. His early familiarity with the English countryside was soon matched by a fascination with Germany, stimulated by walking tours. The knowledge that he gleaned from these travels gave him the authority to represent touchstones of Romanticism, from Andersen to Wagner, in uncanny detail. His vision is so comprehensive and so convincing that it seems we need look just a little harder; if we do, we too would see Shakespeare's fairies playing in the hedgerows and Grimm's goblins looming out from the shadows cast by twisted trees.

For a biography of Arthur Rackham, please refer to *The Illustrators*, 2018, Page 4.

For essays on various aspects of the artist's achievements, see *The Illustrators*, 1997, Pages 124-125; *The Illustrators*, 1999, Pages 98-99; *The Illustrators*, 2000, Pages 14-15; and *The Illustrators*, 2002, Pages 26-27.

His work is represented in numerous public collections, including the British Museum and the V&A; and the Butler Library (Columbia University in the City of New York), The Cleveland Museum of Art (OH), The New York Public Library and the Harry Ransom Humanities Research Center (University of Texas at Austin).

Further reading
James Hamilton, *Arthur Rackham: A Life with Illustration*, London: Pavilion Books, 1990; James Hamilton, 'Rackham, Arthur (b Lewisham, London, 19 Sept 1867; d Limpsfield, Surrey, 6 Sept 1939), Jane Turner (ed), *The Dictionary of Art*, London: Macmillan, 1996, Vol 25, Pages 835-856; James Hamilton, 'Rackham, Arthur (1867-1939)', in H C G Matthew and Brian Harrison (eds), *Oxford Dictionary of National Biography*, Oxford University Press, 2004, Vol 45, Pages 718-721; Derek Hudson, *Arthur Rackham: His Life and Work*, London: Heinemann, 1960

10 THEY WERE RULED BY AN OLD SQUAW SPIRIT WHO HUNG UP THE NEW MOONS IN THE SKIES AND CUT UP THE OLD ONES INTO STARS (opposite)
Signed and dated 1904
Pen ink and watercolour
14 ¼ x 10 ½ inches
Illustrated: Washington Irving, *Rip Van Winkle*,
London: William Heinemann, 1905, [unpaginated]

11 TWO BULLS
Pen and ink
3 x 9 ½ inches
Possibly drawn for but not illustrated in G K Chesterton (intro),
V S Vernon Jones (tr), *Aesop's Fables*, London: William Heinemann, 1912

12 VENICE
Signed and inscribed with title
Watercolour
7 x 10 inches

13 CHRYSANTHEMUMS AND DAISIES (opposite)
Signed
Watercolour on board
13 ¼ x 11 ¼ inches
Provenance: The Estate of Arthur Rackham
Exhibited: 'Arthur Rackham – Illustrations, Drawings and Watercolours',
Graves Art Gallery, Sheffield; Bristol City Art Gallery and Museum;
Victoria and Albert Museum, December 1979-April 1980, No 46

Nos **14-17** are all illustrated in
Eden Phillpotts, *A Dish of Apples*,
London: Hodder & Stoughton, 1921,
[published in black and white and
subsequently coloured by the artist]

14 AN ELF
(opposite, above left)
Signed
Pen ink and watercolour
2 ½ x 3 inches
Illustrated: Page 34, 'Ribston Pippin'

15 THE PYGMY FOLK OF OLD
(opposite, above right)
Signed
Pen ink and watercolour
2 ½ x 3 inches
Illustrated: Page 68, 'Allington Pippin'

16 SAVE WHERE A MOUSE,
IN HOPE OF SEEDS,
HAS TAKEN COURAGE ONE
TO MAR,
BUT LOST THE GAIN
FOR PAIN
(opposite, below left)
Signed
Inscribed 'reduce to 3/4 size'
below mount
Pen ink and watercolour
2 ½ x 3 inches
Illustrated: Page 50, 'Crab Apple'

17 FEET OF MEN
TRAMPLE THE ORCHARD
HERBAGE
(opposite, below right)
Signed
Pen ink and watercolour
2 ¾ x 3 inches
Illustrated: Page 24, 'Cider Makers'

18 A DISH OF APPLES
Eden Phillpotts,
A Dish of Apples, London:
Hodder & Stoughton, [1921]
First edition with dust jacket
78 pages
8 ¼ x 6 ½ inches

19 EAGLE
Pen and ink
2 ¼ x 3 inches
Illustrated: Henrik Ibsen (tr R Farquharson Sharp),
Peer Gynt. A Dramatic Poem, London: Harrap & Co, 1936, Page 63

20 ASLEEP
Signed and inscribed with artist's address on reverse
Pen and ink
2 ¼ x 6 ½ inches
Illustrated: Charles Dickens, *The Chimes*, New York:
The Limited Editions Club, 1931, printed by George W Jones
in London, Page 99

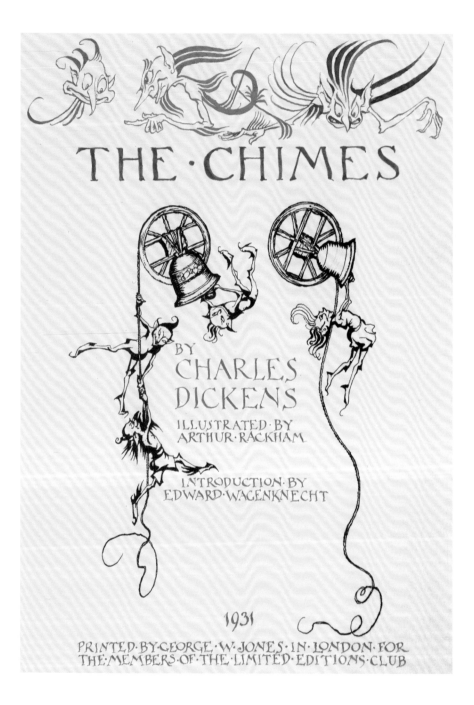

1931 – The Chimes

Nos **20-23** are all illustrated in Charles Dickens, *The Chimes*, New York: The Limited Editions Club, 1931, printed by George W Jones in London

21 IMP
Signed and inscribed with artist's address on reverse
Pen and ink
4 x 3 inches
Provenance: The Estate of Arthur Rackham
Illustrated: Page 51

22 THE CHIMES
Signed and inscribed with artist's address on reverse
Pen and ink on board
10 x 7 ½ inches
Provenance: The Estate of Arthur Rackham
Illustrated: Title page

23 THE GOBLIN OF
THE GREAT BELL
Signed and inscribed with
artist's address on reverse
Pastel
11 ¾ x 7 ¼ inches
Provenance: The Estate of
Arthur Rackham
Illustrated: Page 74
Exhibited: 'Arthur Rackham
– Illustrations, Drawings
and Watercolours', Graves
Art Gallery, Sheffield;
Bristol City Art Gallery and
Museum; Victoria and
Albert Museum, London,
December 1979-April
1980, No 55

The Swallows

William John Hennessy produced this watercolour in October 1871, within a year of his arrival in London from New York, with his new wife, Charlotte, and her sister, Mary. At the time, they were living at the late eighteenth-century Vine House, Chiswick.

Though atypical, the image reveals Hennessy's success at essaying Aestheticism, the artistic credo that was only then gaining in popularity. An elegant lady wears an unstructured dress and stands in an unspecified idyllic landscape. In showing the influence of Japanese art, it may be compared to works by Walter Crane, Albert Moore and Hennessy's friend, James McNeill Whistler. To a degree, the birds and branches presage Crane's 1878 wallpaper design, *Almond Blossom and Swallow*.

24 THE SWALLOWS
Signed
Signed with initials, inscribed 'Vine House Chiswick' and dated 'Oct 1871' below mount
Pen ink, watercolour and bodycolour on tinted paper
13 ½ x 6 ¼ inches
Exhibited: 'The Long Nineteenth Century: Treasures and Pleasures', Chris Beetles Gallery, March-April 2014, No 125

WILLIAM JOHN HENNESSY

William John Hennessy, ROI PS NA (1839-1917)

Irish born William John Hennessy established himself as a painter and illustrator in New York before settling in England in 1870 as a member of a significant expatriate community. He then became well known for a range of genre scenes set in the open air, in a style that synthesised the precision of Pre-Raphaelitism and the atmospherics of French Naturalism, the latter absorbed through long stays in Normandy.

William John Hennessy was born in Thomastown, County Kilkenny, Ireland, on 11 July 1839, the son of John Hennessy and Catherine (née Laffin). John Hennessy's involvement in the Young Ireland movement led to his forced emigration to Canada in 1848. Following his move to New York in 1849, his family joined him and settled in the city.

Receiving his education from private tutors, William Hennessy made his first drawings from life in his early teens. He entered the National Academy of Design late in 1854, and exhibited there regularly between 1857 and 1870.

From 1860, Hennessy gave his exhibition address as the studio complex known as the New York University building. He was elected an associate of the National Academy of Design in 1861 and an academician in 1863. On election, he presented *The Wood Gleaner*, an oil sketch on paper, as a representative example of his work. A founder member of the Artists' Fund Society in 1859, he was invited to join the private club, the Century Association, in 1864, remaining a member for 12 years. The American Society of Painters in Water Colors, founded in 1866, also made him an honorary member.

Developing a skill in wood engraving, Hennessy soon became sought after as an illustrator, especially of the work of poets, and notably of Tennyson and Whittier (for the publisher, Ticknor and Fields). However, 'his most admired work in graphic design' during his American period was perhaps *Mr Edwin Booth in His Various Dramatic Characters*, a volume on the famous actor published in 1872 (Dearinger 2004, Page 261).

In the late 1860s, Hennessy rented a house in Hamden, Connecticut, from the Mather family. He began a relationship with Charlotte Amelia Mather – a noted beauty married to John Ward, a prominent New York surgeon – and had two illegitimate children with her, though neither survived infancy. Following Charlotte's divorce, she and Hennessy married on 19 June 1870. They soon left for Europe, and stayed in Loughton, Essex, before settling in London. Travelling with them was Charlotte's sister, Mary, who would help support them through her articles for *The Atlantic Monthly*. (Five years later, Charlotte's younger brother, Thomas, would marry Margaret Linton,

the daughter of Hennessy's friend and collaborator, the engraver and printer, William James Linton. Linton himself lived in Hennessy's former Hamden home.)

Through the 1870s, Hennessy lived at a number of addresses in Kensington, Chelsea and Chiswick, and developed a social circle that included such expatriate artists as Joseph Pennell and James McNeill Whistler, and also the illustrator, Randolph Caldecott. While continuing to work with American publishers, he established himself in England as both a painter and magazine illustrator. He exhibited landscapes and genre subjects in London, most notably at the Royal Academy (1871-82), and in the provinces, especially in Manchester and Glasgow. He also contributed to *The Dark Blue* (1871-73), *The Graphic* (1872-76; 1880) and *Punch* (1873-75), among other periodicals.

Spending many summers painting the rustic life and landscapes of Normandy, Hennessy began to lease Le Manoir de Pennedepie, Honfleur, near Calvados, in or before 1877. His work began to appear at an increasing number of venues, including the Royal Hibernian Academy, Dublin (1879-1907), and the Grosvenor Gallery and the New Gallery, both in London (the latter opening in 1888). He would become a member of the Pastel Society, the Royal Institute of Oil Painters, the Union Internationale des Beaux Arts et des Lettres, Paris, and also the Savile Club, which he often gave as his London address. As an illustrator, he worked mainly for Macmillan and Co, and particularly on the popular novels of Charlotte M Yonge. He also contributed to *The English Illustrated Magazine* (1884-92) and *Black & White* (1891).

In 1886, Hennessy moved from Honfleur to Saint-Germain-en-Laye, near Paris, settling at the Pavillon Montespan in the Rue de Fourqueux. During his time there, he also toured Italy. In 1893, he returned to England, living in Susssex, first at Brighton and then at Rudgwick, but continuing to spend much time in France. He died at Rudgwick on 27 December 1917.

The Hennessys' only surviving child, Nora, trained in Paris, at the École nationale supérieure des Arts Décoratifs, and also became an artist. She married the painter, Paul Ayshford Methuen, the Fourth Baron Methuen, in 1915, and lived with him at Corsham Court.

Further reading

David Bernard Dearinger (ed), *Paintings and Sculpture in the Collection of the National Academy of Design*, Manchester VT: Hudson Hills Press, 2004, Pages 261-262

For 'A Preliminary Checklist of Books Illustrated by William John Hennessy', please refer to *The Long Nineteenth Century*, Vol 2, London: Chris Beetles Ltd, 2014, Page 66.

EDMUND J SULLIVAN

Edmund Joseph Sullivan,
RWS RE IS (1869-1933)

*'Sullivan was naturally the most gifted
of the younger black-and-white artists of
my time, not excepting Beardsley.'*
(A S Hartrick, *Painter's Pilgrimage Through
Fifty Years*, Cambridge University Press,
1939, page 156)

**E J Sullivan was one of the most
striking and confident illustrators of
his generation, ranging across many
moods and media, and becoming a
particularly influential teacher.**

For a biography of Edmund Joseph Sullivan,
please refer to *The Illustrators*, 2016,
Pages 6-7.

His work is represented in the collections
of the British Museum, the Imperial War
Museum, the National Portrait Gallery
and the V&A; and The Morgan Library &
Museum (New York, NY) and the Harold
B Lee Library (Provo, UT).

Further reading
Percy V Bradshaw, *E J Sullivan and His Work*
(Art of the Illustrator), London: Press Art
School, 1918; Mark Bryant, 'Sullivan, Edmund
Joseph (1869-1933), *Oxford Dictionary of
National Biography*, Oxford University Press,
2004, October 2015, online; James Thorpe,
Edmund Sullivan (English Masters of Black-and-
White), London: Art and Technics, 1948

25 THE RECITAL
Pen ink and watercolour with bodycolour
and pencil
15 ¾ x 11 ¼ inches

26 MY LADY IN TREBLE
Signed and dated '03
Signed and inscribed with title, artist's address and 'price 25
guineas' on reverse
Signed and inscribed with title and artist's address on label of
the Royal Society of Painters in Water-Colours on backboard

Watercolour and bodycolour with pencil on board
15 ¾ x 16 ½ inches
Exhibited: Royal Society of Painters in Water-Colours, 1903;
Southport Art Gallery, 1907; Berlin, 1907

1910 – The French Revolution

Nos **27-29** were all illustrated in Thomas Carlyle, *The French Revolution. A History*, London: Chapman and Hall, 1910

27 THE FLOURISHING OF 'THE FLEUR DE LYS'
(MARIE AND MARAT)
Signed and dated 1909
Inscribed with title and 'The fine flower of corruption and decay'
below mount
Pen and ink on board
11 x 7 ½ inches
Illustrated: Vol I, 'The Bastille', Facing Page 96

28 DEMOCRACY ENTHRONED
Signed and dated 1910
Pen and ink on board
14 ¼ x 10 ¼ inches
Illustrated: Vol II, 'The Constitution', Facing Page 92

29 THE SWORD OF
DAMOCLES
(LOUIS XVI AND
MARIE ANTOINETTE)
Signed and dated 09
Inscribed with title
below mount
Pen and ink on board
12 ¾ x 7 ¾ inches
Illustrated: Vol I,
'The Bastille', Book V,
Chapter II, Facing Page 154

RENÉ BULL
René Bull (1869-1942)

René Bull was an innovative and wide-ranging cartoonist and illustrator, who distinguished himself in three separate areas. He introduced the Caran d'Ache style into Britain, and began a series of 'inventions' that looks forward to the work of Heath Robinson. He produced visual reports on international conflicts as a 'special artist' for *Black & White*. And he was an assured illustrator of fiction for both children and adults.

René Bull was born in Dublin on 11 December 1869, the eldest of four children of Bedford-born Cornelius Bull, owner of a firm of church furnishers, and his French wife, Gabrielle (née Joune). His younger brother was the pioneering chronophotographer, Lucien George Bull. He was educated at Radford House, Coventry (including 1881), Clongowes Wood College, County Kildare (including 1884-85) and the Lycée Janson, Paris.

In about 1890, Bull went to Paris to study engineering. As an uncle of his was on the secretariat of the engineer, Ferdinand de Lesseps, he was offered a job on the building of the Suez Canal. However, fired by a meeting with the famous French cartoonist, Caran d'Ache, he turned this down in order to develop his own skills as a graphic draughtsman. In 1892, he produced the double-page comic, *La peinture fin de siècle*, while still in the French capital, and then returned home to Ireland, where he contributed to the Dublin journal, *Freeman's Weekly*.

Moving to London, Bull contributed to *Illustrated Bits* before meeting Clement Shorter, the editor of *Pick-Me-Up*, newly-launched in 1893; he drew wordless strip cartoons in the style of Caran d'Ache for that magazine (and so introduced the Caran d'Ache style into Britain). In the same year, he married Katharine Shield in Hampstead, but, though they had two daughters, they divorced after three years.

Bull confirmed his talent as a comic draughtsman through a range of magazines, but especially a long series of 'inventions', published in *The Sketch* between 1895 and 1918, which drew on his experience as an engineer and presaged the work of William Heath Robinson. He also drew advertisements, designed comic postcards and contributed to annuals. In 1898, he was a founder member of the London Sketch Club, where he became known as 'an inexhaustible raconteur, a musician, and wizard of ledger-de-main, especially with cards!' (David Cuppleditch, *The London Sketch Club*, Stroud: Alan Sutton Publishing, 1994, Page 47). At this time, he was living at Sunnyside, St Mary's Grove, Gunnersbury, in west London.

In 1896, Bull began to develop a new strand to his talents by working as a 'special artist' for *Black & White*. He made a name for himself by providing a visual report of several international conflicts, in photography and film as well as drawing. These conflicts include the Armenian massacres (1894-96), famine and frontier wars in India (1896-98), the Sudan campaign (1898, for which he was awarded a medal) and the Second Boer War (out of which he was invalided in 1900, and again awarded a medal).

Bull turned to book illustration for both children and adults in 1905, with *La Fontaine's Fables* (illustrated with C Moore Park) and Savile & Watson's *Fate's Intruder*. Early in the following decade, he capitalised on his first-hand knowledge of exotic settings by illustrating *The Arabian Nights* (1912) and *The Rubáiyát of Omar Khayyám* (1913). By 1908, he was living at 10 Palliser Court, Palliser Road, Baron's Court, where, as a model railway enthusiast, he had a track circuiting his dining room. By 1913, he had also acquired Darby Green Farm, Blackwater, Hampshire, and in later years this would become his home.

During the First World War, Bull served in the Royal Naval Volunteer Reserve (1916) and the Royal Flying Corps (1917). Applying his skills as an engineer, it was he who enabled machine guns to be fired through the propellers of fighter planes. His life of adventure extended into the early 1920s when he reported on the Graeco-Turkish War, and spent two nights in the hands of the Turks in Volos, before making his escape.

Between the wars, Bull continued to illustrate books with titles that include Jonathan Swift's *Gulliver's Travels* and Hans Andersen's *Fairy Tales* (both published in 1928). In 1940, he entered service with the Air Ministry and undertook technical duties. However, two years later, on 14 March 1942, he died at home in Hampshire.

30 THE COURT OF THE CALIPH (opposite)
Signed
Watercolour with bodycolour on board
13 ½ x 9 ½ inches
Probably drawn for either *The Arabian Nights*,
London: Constable & Co, 1912, or Edward Fitzgerald,
The Rubáiyát of the Omar Khayyám, London:
Hodder & Stoughton, 1913

FLORENCE HARRISON

Florence Susan Harrison (1877-1955)

The late Pre-Raphaelite illustrations of Florence Harrison have always stood out from those of her contemporaries, the colour plates having the luminosity and strong outlines of stained glass, and the line drawings a decorative efflorescence.

For a biography of Florence Harrison, please refer to *The Illustrators*, 2014, Page 146.

Further reading
Mary Jacobs, 'Florence Susan Harrison', *Studies in Illustration*, Imaginative Book Illustration Society, No 46, winter 2010, Pages 22-59 (with a bibliography of published illustrations)

1907 – The Rhyme of a Run

Nos **31-33** are all illustrated in Florence Harrison, *The Rhyme of a Run*, London: Blackie & Son, 1907, [unpaginated]

31 THERE WE FED ON FROZEN DEW,
AND STRAWBERRIES WILD, AND HONEY TOO
Signed with monogram
Pen ink and watercolour with bodycolour
6 ¼ x 10 inches
Illustrated: *The Rhyme of a Run*, 'Brownie's Park'; Florence Harrison, *Tales in Rhyme and Colour*, London: Blackie and Son, 1916, [unpaginated], 'Brownie's Park'
Exhibited: 'The Turn of Women Artists 1837-2018', Chris Beetles Gallery, March-April 2018, No 101

32 LITTLE BILLY BOATMAN, PUT OUT TO SEA;
I'LL GIVE YOU A PENNY IF YOU'LL TAKE ME
Signed with monogram
Pen ink and watercolour
6 ¼ x 10 inches
Illustrated: *The Rhyme of a Run*, 'Billy Boatman';
Florence Harrison, *Tales in Rhyme and Colour*, London:
Blackie and Son, 1916, [unpaginated], 'Billy Boatman'
Exhibited: 'The Turn of Women Artists 1837-2018',
Chris Beetles Gallery, March-April 2018, No 102

33 TOPPLY TILTS, HE WALKED ON STILTS
Signed with monogram
Inscribed with title on reverse of middle panel
Pen ink and watercolour
6 ½ x 9 ¾ inches
Illustrated: *The Rhyme of a Run*, 'Topply Tilts'

CHARLES FOLKARD
Charles James Folkard (1878-1963)

Influenced by the tradition of the gift book, Charles Folkard became a prolific and imaginative illustrator of attractive children's books, while also creating the influential strip cartoon, 'Teddy Tail'.

Charles Folkard was born in Lewisham, South London, on 6 April 1878, the son of a printer. Educated locally at Colfe's Grammar School, he began an apprenticeship with a firm of designers, but left to become a conjuror. It was in designing programmes for his shows that he discovered his talent for drawing. He then studied at various art schools – including Goldsmiths' College and those at St John's Wood, Blackheath and Sidcup – while beginning to establish a career as an illustrator. Initially contributing humorous drawings to such periodicals as *Little Folks* and *The Tatler*, he made his name, in 1910, with illustrations to an edition of Johann Wyss's *The Swiss Family Robinson*. A year later, he illustrated *The Children's Shakespeare* and *Grimm's Fairy Tales*, so initiating a relationship with the publisher, A & C Black, which would last for 27 years.

In 1915, Folkard joined the *Daily Mail* as a staff artist and, in that position, invented the newspaper's strip cartoon, 'Teddy Tail'. When he decided to concentrate on book illustration, his son, Harry, took over the strip. Another son, Edward, became a sculptor. Having a strong understanding of the appeal of fantasy, he also wrote pantomimes and children's plays.

Folkard lived at Sandy Cross, Heathfield, Sussex, and died on 25 February 1963.

34 THEY SAW THE OGRE STRIDING FROM HILL TO HILL
Signed
Inscribed with title and story title on original
paper cover
Pen ink and watercolour on board
10 x 6 ½ inches
Illustrated: *Mother Goose's Nursery Tales*, Facing Page 48,
'Little Thumbling'

1923 – Mother Goose's Nursery Tales

Nos **34-38** are all illustrated in L Edna Walter (ed), *Mother Goose's Nursery Tales*, London: A & C Black, [1923]

35 AND FOX-LOX SAID, 'COME ALONG WITH ME, AND I WILL SHOW YOU THE WAY'
Signed
Inscribed with story title below mount
Pen ink and watercolour on board
10 x 6 ½ inches
Illustrated: *Mother Goose's Nursery Tales,* Facing Page 108, 'The Story of Chicken-Licken'

36 IN A SHORT TIME HE HAD NO FURTHER DISTURBANCE
FROM THE RATS AND MICE
Pen ink and watercolour on board
16 ¼ x 11 inches
Illustrated: *Mother Goose's Nursery Tales*, Facing Page 88,
'Dick Whittington and his Cat'

37 PRAY, BAKER, GIVE ME SOME BREAD
Signed
Signed and inscribed with artist's address on reverse
Pen ink and watercolour on board
16 ½ x 11 ¼ inches
Illustrated: *Mother Goose's Nursery Tales*, Frontispiece,
'The Cat and the Mouse'

38 HELP! HELP! MY
LORD THE MARQUIS
OF CARABAS IS
DROWNING!
Signed
Inscribed with title and story
title below mount
Pen ink and watercolour
with bodycolour on board
10 x 6 ½ inches
Illustrated: *Mother Goose's
Nursery Tales,* Facing Page 24,
'Puss-in-Boots'

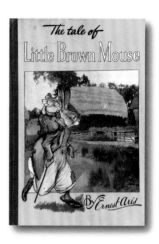

Nos **39-42** are all illustrated in Ernest Aris, *The Tale of Little Brown Mouse*, London: Ward, Lock & Co, 1947

39 PICKING UP LITTLE BROWN MOUSE, HE HOISTED HER UPON HIS SHOULDER
Signed
Inscribed 'Picking up the Little Mouse he hoisted her up on his shoulder'
below mount
Pen ink, watercolour and pencil on paper on board
12 ¼ x 9 ¾ inches
Illustrated: *The Tale of Little Brown Mouse*, Facing Page 27

ERNEST ARIS

Ernest Alfred Walter George Aris, FZS SGA (1882-1963)

As a prolific writer and illustrator for children, Ernest Aris created simple tales about anthropomorphic woodland animals.

Ernest Aris was born in Islington, London, on 22 April 1882, the son of a lithographic artist. During his childhood, his family moved to Bradford, and he first studied at the local Technical College and School of Art, gaining his diploma (1900) under the tutorship of Charles Stephenson. Later, he studied under Gerald Moira, among others, at the Royal College of Art.

Aris began his career as a portrait artist (in charcoal, wash and watercolour), and exhibited work at the Royal Academy, the Royal Society of British Artists, the Royal Society of Painters in Water-Colours and the Royal Institute of Painters in Water-Colours. However, he turned to publishing in the hope of establishing himself more quickly. During this period, he also worked as an art master at the International Correspondence School (1909-12).

Initially contributing to periodicals, Aris illustrated his first books in 1909, including his own text, *My Very Little Book of Animals*, and soon developed into a prolific illustrator – and writer – for children. His simple tales focussed on anthropomorphic woodland animals, the images being grounded in scientific preparatory studies, especially those made while living at Windermere. Beatrix Potter was a neighbour across the lake and, in 1916, Aris was asked to prepare illustrations for her story, 'The Oakmen', though this was never published.

Within a decade, Aris became so productive that he presented numerous stories under various pseudonyms, including Robin A Hood and Dan Crow. He also produced advertisements, cigarette cards, cartoons, games, jigsaw puzzles and postcards (the last using the signature EARIS).

In 1934, Aris was commissioned by Cadbury's to design a range of animal characters that would be made by Britains and given away free with a new line of cocoa. The cast of animals also appeared in Aris's illustrations to a comic, *The Cococub News*.

In 1943, Aris was elected to the membership of the Society of Graphic Artists. His last book as a writer appears to have been a drawing manual, *The Art of the Pen* (1948). However, he continued to illustrate books, including Dorothy Richards' Ladybird series of 'Tasseltip Tales' (1947-53).

Aris died in Hornsey, North London on 14 April 1963.

Further reading
Dudley Chignall, *Ernest Aris* (1882-1963). *The Man Who Drew for Beatrix Potter*, London: Lulu Enterprises, 2010

40 THERE WASN'T A PRETTIER FLOWER IN ALL THE COUNTRYSIDE
Signed
Pen ink, watercolour and pencil with bodycolour and crayon on paper on board
13 x 9 ¾ inches
Illustrated: *The Tale of Little Brown Mouse,* Facing Page 5

41 LITTLE BROWN MOUSE RESCUES THE DANDELION CLOCK FROM THE SPIDER'S WEB
Signed
Inscribed 'Little Wee Wun rescues the dandelion clock from the spider's web' below mount
Pen ink, watercolour and pencil on paper on board
13 ¼ x 9 inches
Illustrated: *The Tale of Little Brown Mouse*, Facing Page 12

42 THEY GATHERED ROUND LITTLE BROWN MOUSE TO THINK UP A PLAN
Signed and dated 46
Inscribed 'They gathered round Wee Wun to think of a plan' below mount
Pen ink, watercolour and pencil with bodycolour and crayon on paper on board
12 ¾ x 10 ½ inches
Illustrated: *The Tale of Little Brown Mouse*, Frontispiece

Nos **43-48** are all illustrated in
Ernest Aris, *The Browns of Brambledown*,
London: Ward, Lock & Co, 1947

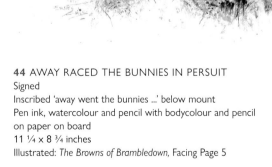

43 THE BROWNS FIND THEIR HOME IN BRAMBLEDOWN
Signed
Inscribed with title below mount
Pen ink, watercolour and pencil with bodycolour and pencil
on paper on board
12 x 9 ¾ inches
Illustrated: *The Browns of Brambledown*, Frontispiece

44 AWAY RACED THE BUNNIES IN PERSUIT
Signed
Inscribed 'away went the bunnies ...' below mount
Pen ink, watercolour and pencil with bodycolour and pencil
on paper on board
11 ¼ x 8 ¾ inches
Illustrated: *The Browns of Brambledown*, Facing Page 5

45 POOR TEDDY, HE WAS WET THROUGH
Signed
Inscribed 'Topsy & Tim had a terrible job to get him out' below mount
Pen ink, watercolour and pencil with bodycolour and pencil
on paper on board
12 ¼ x 9 inches
Illustrated: *The Browns of Brambledown*, Facing Page 12

46 THE FOX PASSED THEM BY
Signed
Inscribed 'Old Fox passes by' below mount
Pen ink, watercolour and pencil with bodycolour and pencil
on paper on board
11 ¾ x 9 ¼ inches
Illustrated: *The Browns of Brambledown*, Facing Page 14

47 IT WAS THE MADDEST, MERRIEST DANCE OF ALL
Signed
Inscribed 'the maddest merriest dance of all' and 'moonlight scene'
below mount
Pen ink, watercolour and pencil with bodycolour and pencil
on paper on board; 11 ¼ x 9 inches
Illustrated: *The Browns of Brambledown*, Facing Page 29

48 MUMSY BROWN PICKED UP HER DARLING BUNNY BABIES
AND CARRIED THEM INTO THE BURROW
Signed
Inscribed with title below mount
Pen ink, watercolour and pencil with bodycolour and pencil
on paper on board ; 11 ¼ x 9 inches
Illustrated: *The Browns of Brambledown*, Facing Page 27

HARRY CLARKE
Henry Patrick Clarke, RHA (1889-1931)

Harry Clarke's ability to work with equal distinction as a book illustrator and stained-glass artist has led to his reputation as a leading figure in the Arts and Crafts movement, not only in his native Ireland but internationally.

For a biography of Harry Clarke, please refer to *The Illustrators*, 2011, Page 78.

Further reading
Nicola Gordon Bowe, *The Life and Work of Harry Clarke*, Blackrock: Irish Academic Press, 1989; Martin Moore Steenson, *A bibliographical checklist of the work of Harry Clarke*, London: Books and Things, 2003

   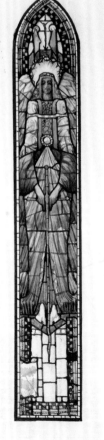

49 TWO SAINTS AND TWO ANGELS: A DESIGN FOR STAINED GLASS WINDOWS
Pen ink and watercolour with bodycolour
7 ¾ x 8 inches

50 THE COLOSSAL WATERS REAR THEIR HEADS ABOVE US LIKE DEMONS OF THE DEEP
(opposite)
Signed with initials
Pen ink, watercolour and bodycolour
15 x 10 ¾ inches
Illustrated: Edgar Allan Poe, *Tales of Mystery and Imagination*, London: George G Harrap & Co, 1923, 'Manuscript Found in a Bottle'

WILLIAM HEATH ROBINSON

William Heath Robinson (1872-1944)

Heath Robinson is a household name, and a byword for a design or construction that is 'ingeniously or ridiculously over-complicated' (as defined by *The New Oxford Dictionary of English*, 1998, Page 848). Yet, he was also a highly distinctive and versatile illustrator, whose work could touch at one extreme the romantic watercolours of a Dulac or Rackham, at another the sinister grotesqueries of a Peake, and at yet another the eccentricities of an Emett.

For a biography of William Heath Robinson, please refer to *The Illustrators*, 2018, Page 22.

Essays on various aspects of Heath Robinson's achievements have appeared in previous editions of *The Illustrators*: on his illustrations to Rabelais in 1996, Pages 112-113; on the relationship of his illustrations to those of Arthur Rackham in 1997, Pages 124-125; on his illustrations to *The Arabian Nights Entertainments* in 1999, Pages 73-74; and on one of his illustrations to *Twelfth Night* in 2000, Pages 17-18.

His work is represented in the collections of the British Museum, The Cartoon Museum, the Heath Robinson Museum and the V&A.

Further reading

Geoffrey Beare, *The Art of William Heath Robinson*, London: Dulwich Picture Gallery, 2003; Geoffrey Beare, *The Brothers Robinson*, London: Chris Beetles Ltd, 1992; Geoffrey Beare, *Heath Robinson Advertising*, London: Bellew, 1992; Geoffrey Beare, *The Illustrations of W Heath Robinson*, London: Werner Shaw, 1983; Geoffrey Beare, *William Heath Robinson 1872-1944*, London: Chris Beetles Ltd, 2011; Langston Day, *The Life and Art of W Heath Robinson*, London: Herbert Joseph, 1947; James Hamilton, *William Heath Robinson*, London: Pavilion Books, 1992; Simon Heneage, 'Robinson, William Heath (1872-1944)', H C G Matthew and Brian Harrison (eds), *Oxford Dictionary of National Biography*, Oxford University Press, 2004, Vol 47, Pages 428-431; John Lewis, *Heath Robinson. Artist and Comic Genius*, London: Constable, 1973

Geoffrey Beare, *The Brothers Robinson*, London: Chris Beetles Ltd, 1992. Fully illustrated catalogue hardback limited to 500 copies, 240 pages

Framed by details of **56**

The Chris Beetles Gallery has mounted a number of significant exhibitions of the work of William Heath Robinson, including:

1. 'William Heath Robinson (1872-1944)', Chris Beetles Gallery, March 1987 (with a fully illustrated catalogue)

2. 'The Brothers Robinson', Chris Beetles Gallery and the Royal Festival Hall, February 1992 (with a fully illustrated catalogue – see further reading and catalogue image)

3. 'William Heath Robinson (1872-1944). 50th Anniversary Exhibition', Chris Beetles Gallery, September 1994

4. 'The Gadget King', Manchester City Art Galleries, Heaton Hall, May-October 2000

5. 'W Heath Robinson', Dulwich Picture Gallery, Linbury Room, November 2003 (to complement Dulwich's own exhibition of William Heath Robinson)

6. 'Heath Robinson at Nunnington Hall', National Trust, Nunnington Hall, North Yorkshire, July 2005

7. 'Contraptions. William Heath Robinson (1872-1944)', Chris Beetles Gallery, June-August 2007 (to launch a volume of cartoons published by Duckworth)

8. 'William Heath Robinson 1872-1944', Chris Beetles Gallery, May-June 2011 (with a fully illustrated catalogue – see further reading)

9. 'The Inventive Art of William Heath Robinson', Chris Beetles Gallery, March-April 2016

1904 – The Works of
Mr Francis Rabelais

Nos **51-55** are all illustrated in
The Works of Mr Francis Rabelais, London:
Grant Richards, 1904, and are all drawn
in pen and ink

51 HE ALSO CAUS'D TO BE
BOUGHT THREE FINE YOUNG
UNICORNS
Signed
Inscribed with title and publication
details below mount
15 ½ x 11 inches
Illustrated: *Rabelais*, Vol II, Page 67

52 THEY FELL TO 'T
Signed and inscribed 'and then fell to 't, squimble, squamble, catch that
catch can. ch. xiii book v'
16 ½ x 11 ½ inches
Illustrated: *Rabelais*, Vol II, Page 245
Exhibited: 'William Heath Robinson 1872-1944', Chris Beetles Gallery,
May-June 2011, No 223

53 HAVING DISCOVER'D AN AMBUSCADE OF
SQUOB-CHITTERLINGS
Signed
Inscribed with title below mount
22 ¼ x 15 ¾ inches
Illustrated: *Rabelais*, Vol II, Page 139
Exhibited: 'William Heath Robinson 1872-1944', Chris Beetles Gallery,
May-June 2011, No 220

54 LOUPGAROU
Signed and inscribed with title
22 ½ x 17 ½ inches
Illustrated: *Rabelais*, Vol I, Page 225
Exhibited: 'William Heath Robinson 1872-1944', Chris Beetles Gallery,
May- June 2011, No 217

55 BRIDLEGOOSE
Signed and inscribed with title and '(ch xxxix book iii)'
19 ¾ x 13 ½ inches
Illustrated: *Rabelais*, Vol II, Page 13

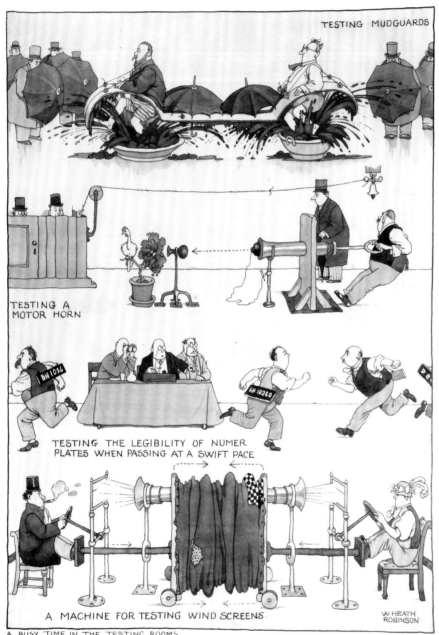

TESTING MUDGUARDS

TESTING A MOTOR HORN

TESTING THE LEGIBILITY OF NUMER PLATES WHEN PASSING AT A SWIFT PACE

A MACHINE FOR TESTING WIND SCREENS

W·HEATH ROBINSON

A BUSY TIME IN THE TESTING ROOMS OF AN UP-TO-DATE MOTOR FACTORY

56 A BUSY TIME IN THE TESTING ROOMS OF AN UP-TO-DATE MOTOR FACTORY
Signed and inscribed with title
Pen ink and watercolour
14 ¾ x 11 inches
Illustrated: *Hutchinson's Magazine,* June 1926, Vol 15, Page 683

57 HOW TO AVOID
CUSTOMS EXACTIONS
WHEN TRAVELLING ON
THE CONTINENT
Signed and inscribed with title
Pen ink and watercolour
on board
15 ¼ x 11 inches
Illustrated: *Bystander*;
Heath Robinson, *Let's Laugh!*
A Book of Humorous Inventions.
With a Forward by K R G Browne,
London: Hutchinson & Co, 1939,
Page 75

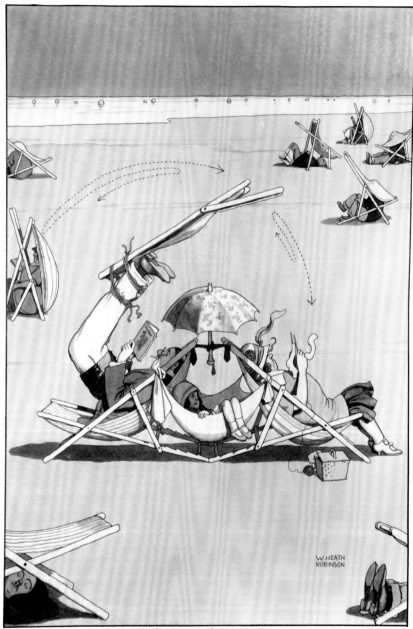

STRENUOUS ENDEAVOURS TO KEEP THE
FAMILY COOL ON A WARM DAY AT SOUTHEND

58 STRENUOUS ENDEAVOURS TO
KEEP THE FAMILY COOL ON A
WARM DAY AT SOUTHEND
Signed and inscribed with title and
'Sunday Graphic'
Pen ink and watercolour
14 ¾ x 10 inches
Illustrated: *Sunday Graphic*, 28 July 1929,
Page 12
Exhibited: 'The Gadget King', Manchester
City Art Galleries, Heaton Hall,
May-October 2000

THE CLOCK BURST
WITH A TERRIFIC CRASH
5.

HEATH
ROBINSON

Nos **60** and **61** are both
illustrated in W H Robinson and
K R G Browne, *How To Be a
Perfect Husband*, London:
Hutchinson & Co, 1937

59 THE CLOCK BURST
WITH A TERRIFIC CRASH
Inscribed with title and '5'
Pen and ink
10 ½ x 7 ¼ inches
Illustrated: Norman Hunter, *The
Incredible Adventures of Professor
Branestawm*, London: John Lane
at the Bodley Head, 1933, Page 65

60 THE TRIP-PRAM
FOR TRIPLETS
Signed
Inscribed with title below mount
Pen and ink on board
5 ½ x 5 ½ inches
Illustrated: Page 66
Exhibited: 'The Inventive Art of
William Heath Robinson', Chris
Beetles Gallery, March-April 2016

61 CONVERTED WEDDING
PRESENTS – THE WATER
BOTTLE HAT
Pen and ink
2 ¼ x 1 ¾ inches
Illustrated: Page 39
Exhibited: 'The Brothers
Robinson', Chris Beetles Gallery,
February-March 1992, No 547

TURNING MINCE PIES FOR THE XMAS MARKET

62 TURNING MINCE PIES FOR THE CHRISTMAS MARKET
Inscribed with title
Pen ink and watercolour
14 x 9 inches
Illustrated: Heath Robinson, *Let's Laugh! A Book of Humorous Inventions. With a Forward by K R G Browne*, London: Hutchinson & Co, 1939, Page 111; *The Penguin Heath Robinson*, London: Penguin 1966, [unpaginated]; *Meals on Wheels*, London: Souvenir Press, 1989, Page 54
Exhibited: 'W Heath Robinson (1872-1944)', Chris Beetles Gallery, March 1987, No 274

COWARDLY MANOEUVRE BY THE FIRST LORD
TO KIDNAP LORD HAW HAW

63 THE UBIQUITOUS
WINSTON: A COWARDLY
ATTEMPT TO KIDNAP
LORD HAW-HAW
Signed and inscribed 'Cowardly
Manoeuvre by the First Lord to
Kidnap Lord Haw Haw'
Inscribed 'To Oliver and Evelyn
with love from Mother'
(Josephine Heath Robinson
[William's wife]) 'To Donald and
Lucy: We are delighted for you
to have this original – Oliver and
Evelyn' on reverse
Pen and ink on board
16 ¼ x 12 ½ inches
Illustrated: *The Sketch*, 24 January
1940, Page 99

FOUGASSE

Cyril Kenneth Bird, CBE (1887-1965), known as 'Fougasse'

As cartoonist, art editor and editor, Cyril Bird transformed the style of *Punch*. His own contributions pared down human activity with such economy as to suggest the essence of modern life. This approach also had a significant influence on advertising, as in the emphasis on the elegant streamlining of Austin Reed's 'New Tailoring'.

For a biography of Fougasse, please refer to *The Illustrators*, 2009, page 77.

His work is represented in the collections of the London Transport Museum and the V&A.

Further reading

Bevis Hillier (ed), *Fougasse*, London: Elm Tree Books, 1977; Peter Mellini, 'Bird, (Cyril) Kenneth [*pseud.* Fougasse] (1887-1965)', H C G Matthew and Brian Harrison (eds), *Oxford Dictionary of National Biography*, Oxford University Press, 2004, Vol 5, Pages 818-820

64 STUNT
Pen and ink
1 ¾ x 3 ¼ inches
Illustrated: *Punch*, 4 January 1956, Page 49

'For most people a note of quiet dignity seemed to have been struck when Miss France of 1955 left a Miami Beach night-club production "because her costumes were too revealing". Only show-business circles are saying that some people will do anything to get their names in the papers.'

65 ORAL DISGUISES
Pen and ink
2 x 3 ¼ inches
Illustrated: *Punch*, 4 September 1963, Page 329

'Trying to evade the press, Mrs Paul Robeson left home wearing a plastic hood and carrying letters between her teeth. This new development in disguise is ingenious and capable of development. Non-smokers could bite pipes, men could grip handles of shopping baskets like well-trained dogs and women could pack their mouths with copies of manly periodicals. Did pirates, perhaps, carry cutlasses between their teeth, not to leave their hands free for boarding ships, but to fox identify parades?'

66 SOUNDPROOF, EVEN
Pen and ink
1 ¾ x 3 ¼ inches
Illustrated: *Punch*, 4 January 1956, Page 49

'Four hundred and six pages and a weight of four and a half pounds for a recent record issue of *The New York Times* suggests an attempt to provide complete privacy at the breakfast table for the whole family.'

67 WILL YE NO' COME BACK AGAIN?
Pen and ink
2 x 3 ¼ inches
Illustrated: *Punch*, 9 March 1960, Page 341

'Recruits to the Royal Navy are said to have read with concern that the new missile-ship London, just laid down at Wallsend, is to have a new type of "homing torpedo".'

68 CURTAIN SPEECH
Pen and ink
2 x 3 ¼ inches
Illustrated: *Punch*, 23 March 1955, Page 359

'Mr Nekrasov said in Stockholm that "the Soviet Union has to-day only one atomic power station with a capacity exceeding 50,000 kilowatts, and that is only an experimental plant." Although Mr Nekrasov is Russia's Minister of Power Stations few people had heard of him before, or are likely to again.'

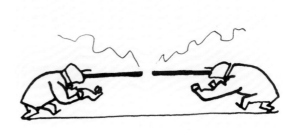

69 YOUR HOLIDAY WEATHER
Pen and ink
2 x 3 ¼ inches
Illustrated: *Punch*, 29 August 1962, Page 289

'A Frenchman has been spending a few weeks down a 400-foot pothole near Nice, studying the physical and psychological effects of "extreme cold, humidity and gloom". In Britain we don't need potholes for this kind of research: surface elements are quite adequate.'

70 STRUGGLE FOR SUPREMACY
Pen and ink
2 x 3 ¼ inches
Illustrated: *Punch*, 22 January 1958, Page 137

'Many sportsmen were misled by a remark in The Times that last week's big fight at the Empress Hall was part of the struggle for supremacy between promoters Levene and Solomons. They had hoped that at last the impresarios themselves would get up there and exchange a bit of punishment.'

71 MAESTROS
III THE SENTIMENTAL:
A CHOPIN NOCTURNE
Signed and dated 1911
Inscribed 'The Sentimentalist'
below mount
Pen ink and watercolour
13 ¼ x 9 ¼ inches
Illustrated: *The Bystander*, Circa 1911;
H M Bateman, *Burlesques*, London:
Duckworth & Co, 1916, Page 7
Literature: Anthony Anderson,
The Man Who Was H M Bateman,
Exeter: Webb & Bower, 1982, Page 41
Exhibited: 'H M Bateman. The Man Who
Went Mad On Paper', The Cartoon
Museum, London, 2012

H M BATEMAN
Henry Mayo Bateman (1887-1970)

H M Bateman established his inimitable style before the First World War when, as he put it, he 'went mad on paper', by drawing people's mood and character. It reached its zenith with 'The Man Who ...', his famous series of cartoons dramatising social gaffes.

For a biography of Henry Mayo Bateman, please refer to *The Illustrators*, 2009, page 72.

For an essay on the revolutionary and reactionary aspects of the artist's work, see *The Illustrators*, 2000, pages 21-22.

His work is represented in numerous public collections, including the British Museum.

Further reading
Anthony Anderson, *The Man Who Was H M Bateman*, Exeter: Webb & Bower, 1982; John Jensen, 'Bateman, Henry Mayo (1887-1970)', H C G Matthew and Brian Harrison (eds), *Oxford Dictionary of National Biography*, Oxford University Press, 2004, Vol 4, Pages 299-301

72 THE STUDENTS
Signed, inscribed with title and dated 1911
Pen ink and watercolour with bodycolour
15 ¼ x 10 inches
Illustrated: *The Bystander*, 28 February 1911
Literature: Anthony Anderson, *The Man Who Was H M Bateman*, Exeter: Webb & Bower, 1982, Page 79 (where it is titled 'Nature Lost in Art'); *H M Bateman the Man Who Went Mad on Paper*, London: Cartoon Museum, 2012, Page 69

73 THE MAN WHO ONLY
WANTED TWO HA'PENNIES
FOR A PENNY!
Signed and dated 1911
Inscribed with title below mount
Pen ink and watercolour with bodycolour
14 x 9 inches
Illustrated: *The Sketch*, 1912, Page 181

74 DOING HIS LITTLE BIT
(THE LITTLE BIT IS INDICATED
BY A X)
Signed with initials and dated 14
Pen and ink on tinted paper
5 ¾ x 13 ¼ inches

75 HE 'OO'-ED TWICE
AND PASSED PEACEFULLY
AWAY
Signed with initials and dated 20
Inscribed with title below mount
Pen and ink with pencil
5 x 7 inches
Illustrated: *The Tatler*, 28 April
1920, Page 112, 'Letters of
Lucille', Part IV, edited by
A M Burrage

76 PREBENDARY ORPINGTON
Signed
Inscribed with title below mount
Pen and ink
9 ¼ x 6 ¾ inches

77 LITTLE LIVES
ESCOGRIFFE LOUPGAROU
Signed and dated 19
Pen and ink with pencil on board
10 x 7 ½ inches

79 THE MAYOR IN MUFTI
Signed
Inscribed with title below mount
Pen and ink with pencil on
tinted paper
13 ¼ x 9 inches

78 THE PLATE JUGGLER
Pen and ink with pencil on
tinted paper
10 ¾ x 6 ¼ inches

80 'THE YARD'
THE BEST DETECTIVES — EDGAR
WALLACE'S — ARE ALWAYS
SCOTLAND YARD MEN
Signed with initials
Inscribed with title below mount
Inscribed with subtitle on reverse
Pen and ink
5 ¼ x 6 ½ inches
Illustrated: *The Strand Magazine*,
June 1929, Page 550, 'About
These Mystery Stories' by
P G Wodehouse

81 THE MAYOR'S PARLOUR
Inscribed with title below mount
Pen and ink
5 x 7 ½ inches

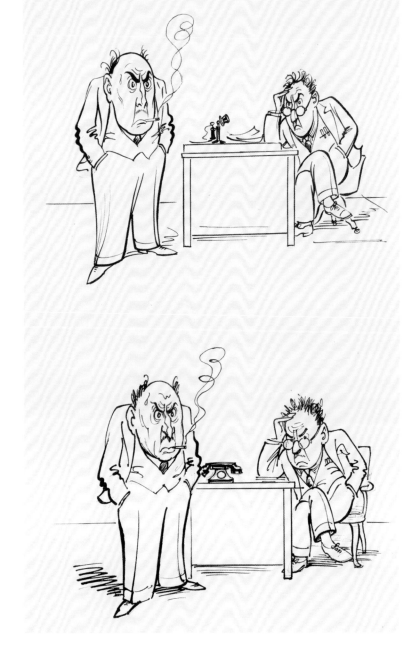

82 EVEN THE WORM DOES A VERY
GOOD TURN
Signed
Pen and ink
9 ½ x 7 ½ inches

83 BUSINESS!
Inscribed with title
Pen and ink with pencil on tinted paper
13 ½ x 8 ¾ inches

84 THE MAN WHO REALLY
BROKE THE BANK AT
MONTE CARLO
Signed
Pen ink and watercolour
14 x 10 inches
Literature: H M Bateman, *Brought
Forward: A Further Collection of
Drawings*, London: Methuen,
1931; Michael Bateman (intro),
*The Man Who Drew the 20th
Century*, London: Macdonald and
Company, 1969

85 IT'S BOUND TO COME
Signed and inscribed with title
Pen and ink
15 ¼ x 10 inches
Illustrated: *London Opinion*,
1 July 1931
Exhibited: 'H M Bateman. The
Man Who Went Mad On Paper',
The Cartoon Museum, 2012

PONT
Gavin Graham Laidler, ARIBA (1908-1940), known as 'Pont'

Following in the *Punch* tradition of George Du Maurier and Frank
Reynolds, Graham 'Pont' Laidler excelled at satirising the British
middle classes. Before his premature death at the age of just 32,
Laidler had established a reputation as one of the finest
cartoonists of the twentieth-century with his acute observations
of 'the British Character'.

For biography of Pont, please refer to *The Illustrators*, 2014, Page 130.

Further reading

Bernard Hollowood, *Pont. The Life and Work of the great Punch artist*, London: Collins,
1969; Richard Ingrams, (rev), 'Laidler, (Gavin) Graham [*pseud.* Pont] (1908–1940)',
H C G Matthew and Brian Harrison (eds), *Oxford Dictionary of National Biography*,
Oxford University Press, 2004, Vol 32, Pages 215-216

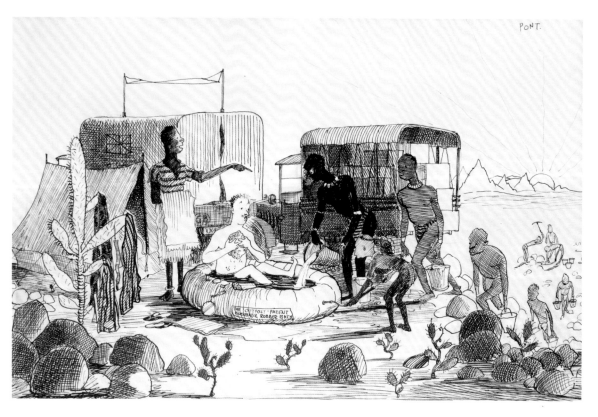

86 NOT EATING YOUR
FAT? AND MILLIONS
STARVING IN RUSSIA!
(opposite above)
Signed and inscribed with title
Pen and ink
4 x 6 inches
Illustrated: *Punch*, 15 June 1938,
page 670
Literature: Bernard Hollowood,
*Pont. The Life and Work of the
great Punch artist*, London:
Collins, 1969, Page 143

87 THE BRITISH
CHARACTER
IMPORTANCE OF THE
MORNING BATH
(opposite below)
Signed
Inscribed with title below mount
Pen and ink
8 x 11 ½ inches

88 THE EDITOR'S
COMPLIMENTS, MY LORD,
AND PLEASE HE WANTS TO
KNOW WHAT YOU WISH
THE NATION TO THINK
ABOUT ON TUESDAY.
Signed
Pen and ink on board
12 ½ x 10 inches
Illustrated: *Punch*, 28 October
1936, Page 487
Exhibited: 'The World of Pont',
The Cartoon Museum, London,
2008, April-May 1983, No 78

E H SHEPARD

Ernest Howard Shepard, MC OBE (1879-1976)

While E H Shepard is now best remembered for his immortal illustrations to *Winnie-the-Pooh* and *The Wind in the Willows*, he was a wide-ranging illustrator, with an unsurpassed genius for representing children, and an underrated talent for political cartoons.

For a biography of E H Shepard, please refer to *The Illustrators*, 2018, Page 41.

For essays on various aspects of the artist's achievements, see *The Illustrators*, 1999, Pages 151-152; *The Illustrators*, 2000, Pages 28-32; and *The Illustrators*, 2007, Pages 199-200.

His work is represented in the collections of the V&A; and the Shepard Archive at the University of Surrey (Guildford).

Further reading
Arthur R Chandler, *The Story of E H Shepard: the man who drew Pooh*, West Sussex: Jaydem, 2001; Rawle Knox (ed), *The Work of E H Shepard*, London: Methuen, 1979; C A Parker (rev), 'Shepard, Ernest Howard (1879-1976)', H C G Matthew and Brian Harrison (eds), *Oxford Dictionary of National Biography*, Oxford University Press, 2004, Vol 50, Pages 230-231

89 LADY (CONCERNED FOR HER VALUABLE PERSIAN RUG TO NEW CHARWOMAN): 'AND, MRS SCOLES, PLEASE BE CAREFUL WITH THIS RUG, IT IS VERY OLD.'
MRS SCOLES: 'THAT IT IS, MUM, BUT I DESSAY WE CAN MAKE IT LAST YOU THE WINTER.'
Signed
Inscribed with title below mount
Pen and ink with bodycolour
9 ½ x 12 inches
Illustrated: *Punch*, 13 December 1922, page 563

90 STRANDED TRAVELLER (MILES FROM ANYWHERE):
'EXCUSE ME, BUT MY CAR HAS BROKEN DOWN. DO YOU
KNOW ANYTHING ABOUT FORDS?'
PASSING MOTORIST: 'AWFULLY SORRY. I'M AFRAID I KNOW
NOTHING ABOUT FORD; EXCEPT, OF COURSE, TWO
FRIGHTFULLY FUNNY STORIES.'
Signed
Inscribed with title below mount
Pen and ink
8 ½ x 12 ¾ inches

Illustrated: *Punch*, 1 October 1924, Page 368; *Fun and Fantasy. Drawings
From Punch* by Ernest H Shepard, London: Methuen, 1927, Page 75
Exhibited: 'E H Shepard at Punch, 1907-1952', Chris Beetles Gallery,
July 2019

Mr Coggs
Again

If any of our watches stop
  We haste to Mr Coggs's shop,
For though to scold us he pretends,
He's quite among our special friends.

He fits a dice box in his eye,
And takes a long and thoughtful spy,
And prods the wheels and says,"Dear, dear!
More carelessness I greatly fear!"

And then he lays the dice box down
And frowns a most prodigious frown;
But if we ask him what's the time
He'll make his gold repeater chime.

91 MR COGGS AGAIN
Signed
Pen and ink
10 ½ x 17 ½ inches
Illustrated: E V Lucas, *Playtime and Company. A Book for Children*,
London: Methuen & Co, 1925, Pages 44-45

Our Cobbler

His back is bent, his knees are stiff,
  He has the dimmest sight;
He soles and heels our boots and shoes
  From early morn till night;
To see him take a holiday
  Would give the town a fright.

And yet there's nothing in the world
  Our cobbler doesn't know;
He knows when circuses are due
  And where good mushrooms grow;
He knows how many Hobbs has made,
  And when it's going to snow.

He knows why Dobson's horse was sold;
  He knows the price it brought;
He knows who's taken Winsome Grange,
  And how the thieves were caught;
He knows who called the doctor up,
  And why those navvies fought.

92 OUR COBBLER
Signed
Pen and ink
11 x 17 ½ inches
Illustrated: E V Lucas, *Playtime and Company. A Book for Children*,
London: Methuen & Co, 1925, Pages 22-23

93 AT THIS POINT JERRY
COLLAPSED FORWARD
Signed with initials
Signed and inscribed and artist's address on reverse
Pen and ink on board
5 x 5 inches
Illustrated: *The Golden Age*, Page 47

94 PUSHED OFF THE EMPTY BOAT WITH HIS
FOOT
Signed and inscribed with artist's address on reverse
Pen and ink with bodycolour and pencil on board
6 ½ x 9 inches
Illustrated: *The Golden Age*, Page 105

95 WITH A LIGHT HEART I TURNED TO AND
STRUMMED
Pen and ink
5 x 4 inches
Illustrated: *The Golden Age*, Page 77

Nos **93-96** are all illustrated in
Kenneth Grahame, *The Golden Age*,
London: John Lane, The Bodley
Head, 1928

96 YOU MIGHT HAVE BEEN
TAKEN AND SHOT AS SPIES
Signed with initials and inscribed
'The Golden Age' below mount
Signed and inscribed with artist's
address on reverse
Pen and ink with pencil on board
11 × 8 inches
Illustrated: *The Golden Age*,
Page 33

97 I THINK IT'S A DRAGON
Signed and inscribed with artist's address on reverse
Pen and ink with bodycolour and pencil on board
5 x 7 ½ inches
Illustrated: Kenneth Grahame, *Dream Days*, London: John Lane, The Bodley Head, 1930, Page 112

98 THE RELUCTANT DRAGON
Signed and inscribed with artist's address on reverse
Pen and ink with bodycolour on board
6 x 11 inches
Illustrated: Kenneth Grahame, *Dream Days*, London: the Bodley Head, 1930, Pages 110-111

SUNDAY NIGHT RETURN

The Sunday train loiters back to London
  Through the sad wet evening of a summer's day.
Close we sit adding at every station
  Of the slow, slow way.

Two men, who've sat contentedly
  Under a railway bridge fishing for hours
Nod, as do the rest of us over our
  Bunches of flowers

The youthful lovers lean against each other,
  Hands entwined, enjoying their small sorrow
Of parting, already divided seeing
  Monday to-morrow.

For this slow journey we are bound in warmth
  Postponing the discomfort that must lie ahead,
Bridging this seated snugness to the coming bliss
  Of ultimate bed

Across the horrid seas of Sunday night
  In a wet city under slanting rain,
Carrying ourselves, our bags and these tired flowers
  Till we are home again.

J. G.

99 SUNDAY NIGHT RETURN
Signed
Inscribed with title below mount
Pen and ink on board
11 x 18 inches
Illustrated: *Punch*, 28 September 1949, Pages 352-353, 'Sunday Night Return' by J G [Joyce Grenfell]
Exhibited: 'E H Shepard at *Punch*, 1907-1952', Chris Beetles Gallery, July 2019

CHARLES TUNNICLIFFE

Charles Frederick Tunnicliffe, OBE RA RE VPSWLA
(1901-1979)

One of the foremost wildlife artists of the twentieth century,
Charles Tunnicliffe displayed his talents in an impressive range of
formats and media, including watercolours, oils, etchings and
wood engravings.

For a biography of Charles Tunnicliffe, please refer to *The Illustrators*, 2018,
Page 62.

Further reading

Ian Niall, *Portrait of a Country Artist: Charles Tunnicliffe, RA, 1901-1979*, London:
Gollancz, 1983; Kyffin Williams (rev), 'Tunnicliffe, Charles Frederick (1901-1979)',
H C G Matthew and Brian Harrison (eds), *Oxford Dictionary of National Biography*,
Oxford University Press, 2004, Vol 55, Pages 550-551

100 TARKA AND THE OWL
(opposite)
Signed with initials
Inscribed 'Magic of Literature 2' on original
supporting card
Pen and ink on scraperboard
7 ½ x 5 inches
illustrated: Robert H Cowley (ed), *The Magic of
Literature. A Miscellany for Boys and Girls*, Book 2,
London: Blackie, 1940, Page 209, 'Tarka the Otter'
by Henry Williamson

Tarka and the Owl
'The Magic of Literature' was a series of four
illustrated miscellanies with study sections for
children of post-primary age. It was compiled by
Robert H Crowley and published in London by
Blackie & Son in the 1940s. For Book 2, published
in 1940, Tunnicliffe contributed an illustration to an
extract from Henry Williamson's *Tarka the Otter*.
Eight years earlier, he had made his name with his
wood-engraved illustrations to Williamson's novel.

101 THE EAGLE I (right)
Inscribed 'Everest V' on original supporting card
Pen and ink on scraperboard
4 x 3 ¾ inches
Probably illustrated in *The Everest Reader* V,
Bombay: Blackie & Son, Circa 1942

102 OUR LITTLE ONES WILL NEVER GROW UP SO LONG AS THAT SNAKE LIVES NEAR US
Inscribed with title and 'The Wise Crow' on original supporting card
Pen and ink on scraperboard
3 ½ x 4 inches
Probably illustrated in *The Everest Reader* III, Bombay: Blackie & Son,
Circa 1942

According to an advertisement in *The South India Teacher* in 1942, 'The Everest Readers' were published in India by Blackie & Son as a 'New Modern and Carefully Graded Series of Readers for Indian Schools' and 'Fully Illustrated in Colour and Black and White'. The illustrations by Charles Tunnicliffe that are represented here suggest that the readers comprised a combination of English and Indian poetry and prose. These included poems by Tennyson ('The Eagle') and Sarojini Naidu ('Spring'), and stories from the ancient Sanskrit collection ('The Crows and the Serpent').

103 SPRING
Inscribed with title, 'Sarojini Naidu' and 'Everest V'
on original supporting card
Pen and ink on scraperboard
3 ¼ x 4 ¼ inches
Probably illustrated in *The Everest Reader* V, Bombay:
Blackie & Son, Circa 1942

104 THE PRINCE'S
SERVANTS SAW THE CROW
DROPPING THE GOLD
ANKLET INTO THE HOLE
IN THE TREE
Inscribed with title and
'Everest Reader III' on original
supporting card
Pen and ink on scraperboard
2 ½ x 4 inches
Probably illustrated in *The Everest
Reader* III, Bombay: Blackie &
Son, Circa 1942

EDWARD ARDIZZONE

Edward Ardizzone, CBE RA RDI (1900-1979)

Highly observant and immensely humane, the work of Edward Ardizzone is in direct descent from the finest French and English illustrators of the nineteenth century. Developing as an artist from 1930, Ardizzone made his name as an illustrator through his contributions to *The Radio Times* and then with *Little Tim and the Brave Sea Captain*, which proved to be one of the most significant picture books published between the wars. Soon considered one of the greatest illustrators of his generation, he also gained a reputation as an Official War Artist. Versatile and productive, he produced paintings, sculptures, etchings and lithographs, and worked as a designer.

Edward Ardizzone was born in Haiphong in French Indo-China on 16 October 1900, to a Franco-Italian father and a Scottish mother. The family returned to England in 1905, and lived first in East Anglia and later in London. However, Ardizzone was educated away from home, at Clayesmore School in the Thames Valley. Working as a statistical clerk from the age of 19, he took evening classes at the Westminster School where he studied under Bernard Meninsky. After seven years, he decided to take up an artistic career as a freelance painter and illustrator in watercolour and pen, and began to exhibit in solo shows at the Bloomsbury (1930) and Leger Galleries (1931-36). Synthesising the bulk of Meninsky's figures with the humour and facility of classic French and English illustrators, he moved from the tight, sinister vignettes of *In a Glass Darkly* (1929) to more typically generous draughtsmanship, achieving widespread recognition with *Little Tim and the Brave Sea Captain* (1936), the first of many books that he both wrote and illustrated. He reached a particularly wide public through his regular contributions to such periodicals as *The Radio Times* and *The Strand Magazine*. Soon considered one of the greatest illustrators of his generation, he also gained a reputation as a distinguished Official War Artist, through his record in word and image of action in North Africa and Europe.

After the Second World War, Ardizzone worked increasingly as an illustrator of literary classics, and collaborated closely with a number of contemporary authors. A teacher of illustration at Camberwell School of Art and of etching at the Royal College of Art (1953-61), he won several prizes including the Carnegie Medal (1955) and the Hans Christian Andersen Medal (1956) for Farjeon's *The Little Bookroom*, and the first Kate Greenaway Award (1956) for *Tim All Alone*. Working additionally as painter, sculptor, lithographer and designer, he became an associate of the Royal Academy in 1962 and a full academician in 1970. He was created CBE in 1971 and a Royal Designer to Industry three years later. Though he lived in Maida Vale for most of his career, he spent an increasing amount of his final decade in Kent, revisiting the coast and countryside that had long inspired him. He died in that county, at Rodmersham, on 8 November 1979.

For an essay on Ardizzone's illustrations to Cyril Ray's *Merry England*, see *The Illustrators*, 1999, Pages 193-195.

His work is represented in numerous public collections, including the British Museum, the Imperial War Museums, Tate and the V&A; and the Ashmolean Museum (Oxford).

Further reading

Brian Alderson, *Edward Ardizzone: A Bibliographic Commentary*, London: The British Library, 2002; Nicholas Ardizzone, *Edward Ardizzone's World. The Etchings and Lithographs. An Introduction and Catalogue Raisonné*, London: Unicorn Press and Wolseley Fine Arts, 2000; Alan Powers, *Edward Ardizzone. Artist and Illustrator*, London: Lund Humphries, 2016; Gabriel White, *Edward Ardizzone*, London: Bodley Head, 1979

105 THE COCKNEY SCENE IN THE 1860S (opposite)
Signed with initials
Inscribed with title and 'Strand Mag' below mount
Pen ink and watercolour with pencil
10 ¾ x 9 inches
Illustrated: *The Strand Magazine*, June 1942, 'The Eternal Cockney'
by Thomas Burke

Nos **105**, **109**, **113-118**, **120**, **124-128**, **129**, **131**, **132** & **137-142** are all from the collection of Judy Taylor MBE, Children's Editor for Bodley Head

Detail of **117**

106 UNDER THE GREENWOOD TREE
Signed 'Diz'
Also stamped with the artist's studio stamp
Pen and ink
6 ½ x 8 inches
Illustrated: *Radio Times*, 30 December 1938, Page 45,
'Under the Greenwood Tree. Thomas Hardy's novel is
to be read as a serial by V C Clinton-Baddeley.'

107 OLD-TIME MUSIC-HALL
Inscribed with title and 'Tel Supplement' and dated 26.3.37 and
3.6.38 on reverse
Pen ink and watercolour with pencil
6 ¼ x 7 ½ inches
Illustrated: *Radio Times*, Television Supplement, 26 March 1937, Page 2,
'Old-Time Music Hall'; *Radio Times*, 3 June 1938, Page 58,
'The Old Music-Halls'

108 THE ESCAPOLOGIST
Pen ink and watercolour with pencil
8 ¼ x 9 ½ inches

109 THE BOAT TO GREENWICH
Signed with initials
Watercolour and pencil
14 x 19 inches

Exhibited: Leicester Galleries, London, February 1948, No 3;
Campbell & Franks (Fine Arts), London, March 1979, No 24;
'Ardizzone by the Sea', Middlesbrough Borough Council Museums and Art
Gallery Service, 1982, No 3

110 SALOON BAR AT THE LOCAL
Inscribed with title on reverse
Inscribed with title on label on original backboard
Pen ink and watercolour
7 ¾ x 11 ¼ inches
Provenance: The Leicester Galleries, London

111 A TOAST AT THE BAR
(opposite)
Signed with initials
Watercolour with ink and pencil on board
10 x 9 ¼ inches

The Private Bar at the Goat

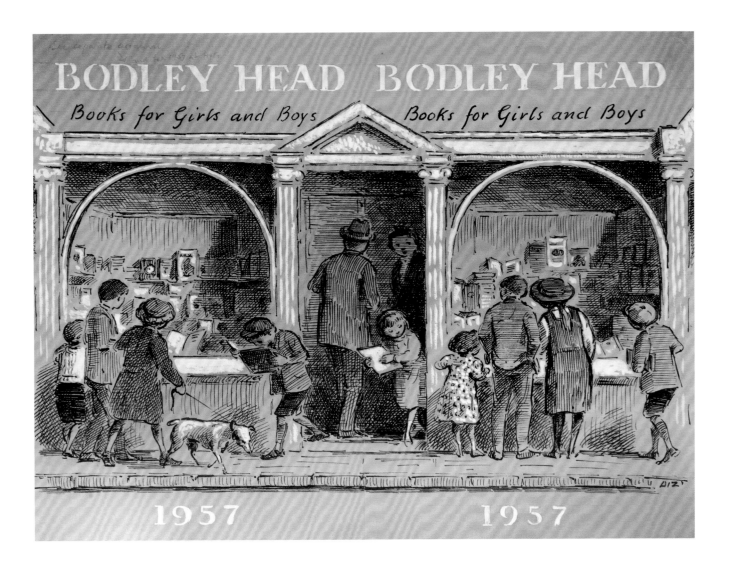

112 THE PRIVATE BAR AT THE GOAT (opposite)
Pen and ink
8 ½ x 5 ¼ inches
Illustrated: Maurice Gorham, *Back To the Local*, London: Percival Marshall,
1949, Page 59
Exhibited: 'Edward Ardizzone', the Scottish Arts Council, Touring Exhibition,
1979-80, No 96; Edward Ardizzone 1900-1979', New Grafton Gallery,
February-March 1981, No 32

113 BODLEY HEAD BOOKS FOR GIRLS AND BOYS
Signed 'Diz'
Pen and ink with bodycolour and pencil on tinted paper
12 x 14 ¾ inches

114 THE BELLES OF ST TRINIAN'S
Signed 'Diz'
Also inscribed by Ronald Searle, 'Edward Ardizzone'
Preliminary pen ink and pencil drawing for 'Girls! Girls!' on reverse
Pen and ink
6 ¼ x 8 ¼ inches
Provenance: Ronald Searle; Judy Taylor MBE
Illustrated: *Punch*, 7 April 1954, Page 435, 'Girls! Girls!' by G W Stonier

Nos **114-116** accompany an article by G W Stonier on his visit to the set of Launder and Gilliat's *The Belles of St Trinian's*, the first of the St Trinian's films, inspired by the creation of Ronald Searle and released in 1954. They were all exhibited at 'Edward Ardizzone RA 1900-1979 – A Centenary Celebration', Ashmolean Museum, Oxford, 2000, No 19

115 THREE ST TRINIAN'S GIRLS
Pen and ink
1 ½ x 2 ¾ inches
Provenance: Ronald Searle; Judy Taylor MBE
Illustrated: *Punch,* 7 April 1954, Page 435, 'Girls! Girls!'
by G W Stonier

116 GIRLS! GIRLS!
Inscribed and dated by Ronald Searle, 'Punch 1954'
Pen and ink
3 ¾ x 8 inches
Provenance: Ronald Searle;
Judy Taylor MBE
Illustrated: *Punch*, 7 April 1954, Page 434, 'Girls! Girls!'
by G W Stonier

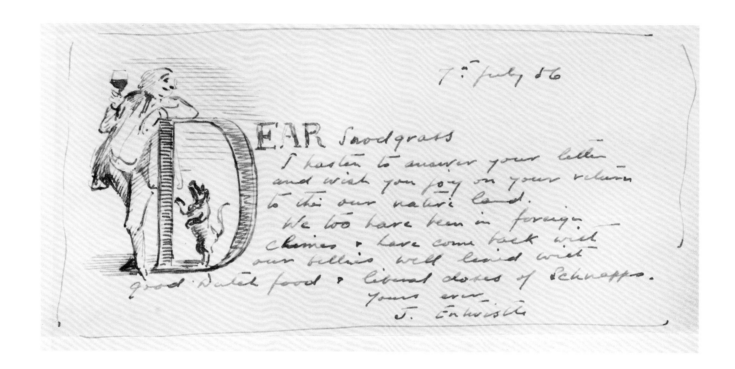

Nos **117-119**: Judy Taylor, in her edition of Ardizzone's *Sketches for Friends*, London: John Murray, 2000, notes that 'in 1959, for his own amusement, Edward Ardizzone began a series of illustrated letters to Mr Snodgrass, an imaginary (and extremely inefficient) publicity manager for a firm of corset manufacturers, Comfi-Corsets.'

117 A LIBERAL DOSE OF SCHNAPPES:
A LETTER TO MR SNODGRASS FROM J ENTWISTLE
Dated '7th July 56'
Pen and ink
4 × 8 inches
Provenance: The Mayor Gallery, July 1980; Judy Taylor MBE

'Dear Snodgrass
I hasten to answer your letter and wish you joy on your
return to this our native land.
We too have been in foreign climes & have come back with our own bellies
well lined with good Dutch food & liberal doses of Schnapps.
Yours ever
J Entwistle'

118 ON BENDED KNEE:
A LETTER TO MR SNODGRASS FROM JOHN PODSNAP
Signed with initials
Pen and ink
4 ¼ × 8 inches

'My dear Snooks
"Rebus in Arduis" I know your difficulties are great but don't forget its 'Aequam memento'. Keep calm, face up to them and problems that seem inseparable now will melt away before a steadfast front.
With best wishes
John Podsnap'

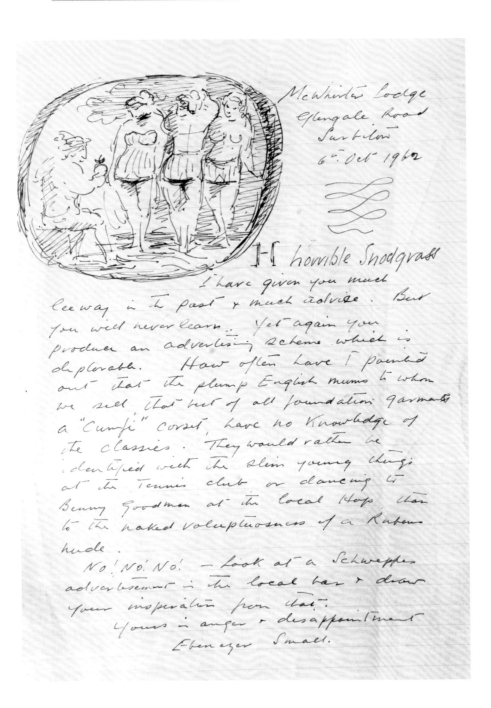

119 THE THREE GRACES:
A LETTER TO MR SNODGRASS
FROM EBENEZER SMALL
Dated '6th Oct 1962'
Pen and ink
10 ½ x 7 ¾ inches

'McWhirter Lodge
Glengale Road
Surbiton

Oh horrible Snodgrass I have given you much leeway in the past & much advice. But you will never learn. Yet again you produce an advertising scheme which is deplorable. How often have I pointed out that the plump English mums to whom we sell that best of all foundation garments a 'Cumfi' corset, have no knowledge of the classics. They would rather be identified with the slim young things at the tennis club or dancing to Benny Goodman at the local Hop than to the naked voluptuousness of a Rubens nude.
No! No! No! – Look at a Schweppes advertisement in the local bar & draw your inspiration from that.
Yours in anger & disappointment
Ebenezer Small'

120 THE ART EXPERT
Pen ink and watercolour with pencil
7 x 6 ½ inches
Provenance: Charles J Sawyer, March 1980; Judy Taylor MBE
Exhibited: 'Edward Ardizzone RA 1900-1979 –
A Centenary Celebration', Ashmolean Museum, Oxford, 2000, No 18

121 LOOKING AT
THE LEONARDOS
Signed with initials
Inscribed 'Looking at the
Michael Angelo drawings'
on reverse
Inscribed with title on label
on original backboard
Pen ink and watercolour
6 ½ x 9 inches

122 MEN LOOKING FOR BAIT
Signed with initials
Inscribed with title on reverse
Pencil drawing of bathers on reverse
Inscribed with title on label on original backboard
Pen ink and watercolour with pencil
7 x 10 inches

Ardizzone produced a lithograph of this composition, entitled *Hunting for Bait*, in 1958. See Nicholas Ardizzone, *Edward Ardizzone's World. The Etchings and Lithographs. An Introduction and Catalogue Raisonné*, London: Unicorn and Wolseley Fine Arts, 2000, No 29

123 ON THE BEACH
Signed with initials
Watercolour and pencil on paper laid on board
5 x 10 ¼ inches

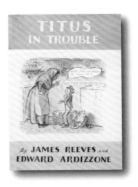

Nos **124** and **125** are illustrated in James Reeves, *Titus in Trouble*, London: Bodley Head, 1959, [unpaginated]

124 SO YOU LIKES A SONG DOES YOU?
Inscribed '16'
Pen ink and watercolour
6 x 6 ½ inches

125 EVERYONE SAID GOOD-BYE AMID LAUGHTER AND TEARS OF JOY
Pen ink and watercolour with pencil
6 ½ x 15 ½ inches

126 TITUS IN TROUBLE
Inscribed with extensive printing and
publication instructions on reverse
Pen ink and watercolour with pencil
10 x 6 ¼ inches
Preliminary drawing for *Titus in Trouble*

127 HE TOLD HER THE WHOLE
SAD STORY
Inscribed with title
Inscribed with printing instructions
below mount
Pen ink and watercolour with pencil
6 ½ x 6 ½ inches
Preliminary drawing for *Titus in Trouble*

128 POOR TITUS HAD TO GIVE
HER FIVE SHILLINGS OF HIS
WEEK'S MONEY TO BUY SOME
MORE FRUIT
Pen ink and watercolour with pencil
8 ½ x 4 inches
Preliminary drawing for *Titus in Trouble*

He told her the whole sad story

129 HERE COMES THE COPPER
Inscribed by John Ryder on reverse, 'Drawn in 1960 by E A for
Artists of a Certain Line given to the author & presented by him
in 1981 to his friend colleague and collector Judy'.
Pen and ink
8 ¼ × 6 inches
Illustrated: John Ryder, *Artists of a Certain Line. A selection of
illustrations for children's books*, London: The Bodley Head, 1960,
Page 44, as 'Imaginative Drawing'

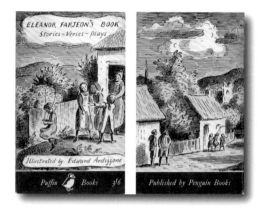

130 OH NO, NO, NO! SHE IS SO DEAR!
SO DEAR SHE IS WHO LIETH HERE
Inscribed with title below mount
Pen and ink
5 × 5 ¾ inches
Illustrated: Eleanor Graham (ed), *Eleanor Farjeon's Book: stories, verses, plays*,
Harmondsworth: Puffin Books, 1960, Page 53, 'Snow-White'

132 DIANA AND HER RHINOCEROS
Pen ink and watercolour with pencil
4 ½ x 4 inches
Preliminary drawing for Edward Ardizzone, *Diana and her Rhinoceros*,
London: Bodley Head, 1964, [unpaginated]

131 MRS EFFINGHAM-JONES CRIED, 'OOEE! OOEE! IT'S EATEN
THE BABY', AND FELL TO THE FLOOR IN A DEADLY FAINT
Inscribed with book title and printing instructions below mount
Pen ink and watercolour with pencil
4 ½ x 4 inches
Preliminary drawing for Edward Ardizzone, *Diana and her Rhinoceros*,
London: Bodley Head, 1964, [unpaginated]

Nos **133-136** are all illustrated in Eleanor Farjeon, *Mrs Malone*, Oxford University Press, 1962, [unpaginated]

133 SHE THREW THE DOOR OPEN AND WARMED UP SOME PAP, AND HUDDLED AND CUDDLED IT IN HER OLD LAP
Pen and ink
3 ½ x 4 inches

134 WHERE AM I, TO GOODNESS, AND WHAT DO I SEE?
MY DEARS, LET'S TURN BACK, THIS AIN'T NO PLACE FER ME!
Inscribed with title below mount
Pen and ink
5 x 6 inches

135 THERE WAS WAILING AND WHINING
OUTSIDE IN THE WOOD,
AND THERE SAT A VIXEN
WITH SIX OF HER BROOD
Inscribed with title below mount
Pen and ink
4 ½ x 5 ½ inches

136 COME SATURDAY EVENING
WHEN TIME WAS TO SUP
MRS MALONE
HAD FORGOT TO SIT UP
Inscribed with title below mount
Pen and ink
3 ½ x 6 inches

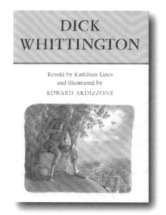

137 HE WALKED UNTIL HE CAME TO HIGHGATE HILL AND THERE HE SAT DOWN ON A STONE (below left)
Pen ink and watercolour
4 ½ x 4 inches
Preliminary drawing for Kathleen Lines (reteller), *Dick Whittington*, London: The Bodley Head, 1970, Front Cover

138 HE MET A GIRL CARRYING A CAT IN HER ARMS
Pen ink and watercolour with pencil
4 x 4 inches
Preliminary drawing for Kathleen Lines (reteller), *Dick Whittington*, London: The Bodley Head, 1970, Page 17

ROWLAND EMETT
Frederick Rowland Emett, OBE (1906-1990)

Rowland Emett established himself as the creator of elegant and whimsical cartoons during the 1930s, while working as an industrial draughtsman. In 1951, he reached a wider public with his designs for The Far Tottering and Oyster Creek Railway, which was sited at Battersea Park during the Festival of Britain. Gradually, he converted more of his illustrations into increasingly complex three-dimensional machines. Both drawings and inventions helped cheer a nation fed up with years of austerity.

Rowland Emett was born in New Southgate, London, on 22 October 1906, the elder son of the proprietor of a small advertising business. Educated at Waverley Grammar School, Birmingham, he showed his father's enthusiasm for invention, and registered his first patent at the age of fourteen. However, he had ambitions to be a landscape painter and studied with great success at the Birmingham School of Art. The combination of artistic and scientific talents allowed Emett to work as an industrial draughtsman while contributing with increasing regularity to *Punch*, *Lilliput* and other magazines from the late 1930s.

During the Second World War, Emett worked as a draughtsman on the development of jet engines. In 1941, he was chosen to illustrate *Bells and Grass*, a series of humorous rhymes that Walter de la Mare had originally written for *Punch*. The poet was so impressed by the result that he immediately encouraged Emett to illustrate an edition of his more famous book, *Peacock Pie*. In the same year, Emett married, and he and his wife set about producing the delightful children's book, *Anthony and Antimacassar* (1943). About the same time, Emett's cartoons began to be collected in volume form, *A Book of Curious Happenings* (1943) initiating a series that culminated in *Far Twittering* (1949).

In 1951, Emett reached a wider public with his designs for The Far Tottering and Oyster Creek Railway, and its featured engine, Nellie, which was sited at Battersea Park during the Festival of Britain. As his eyes faltered, he converted more of his illustrations into increasingly complex three-dimensional machines that, from 1956, he constructed himself at a blacksmith's forge near his home in West Sussex. He received international success, through his work on the film, *Chitty Chitty Bang Bang* (1968), when he gave substance to the adventures of the inventor, Caractacus Potts. He achieved this by employing a team of assistants to help him make eight of his machines for the filming and a further thirty-seven for international promotional purposes. These and other inventions continue to prove popular throughout the world and remain on public exhibition in such esteemed institutions as the National Air and Space Museum in Washington.

A parodist of the real world of functional engineering, Emett had long proved to be the Genius of British Eccentricity, a fact acknowledged by his being awarded an OBE in 1878. This was confirmed by the overwhelming response to the most important exhibition of his career, 'Rowland Emett: From Punch to Chitty-Chitty-Bang-Bang' at the Chris Beetles Gallery in 1988 and, augmented by a number of the machines, at the Smithsonian Museum in Washington. He died on 13 November 1990 in a nursing home in Hassocks, Sussex, close to Wild Goose Cottage, his home in Ditchling.

His work is represented in the collections of The Cartoon Museum, Tate and the V&A. His open air sculptures can be seen at the Victoria Centre, Nottingham and Eastgate Shopping Centre, Basildon; and at the Mid America Science Museum (Hot Springs, Arkansas) and the Ontario Science Centre (Toronto).

Further reading:
Jacqui Grossart, *Rowland Emett: From 'Punch' to 'Chitty-Chitty-Bang-Bang' and beyond*, London: Chris Beetles Ltd, 1988; John Jensen, 'Emett, (Frederick) Rowland (1906-1990)', H C G Matthew and Brian Harrison (eds), *Oxford Dictionary of National Biography*, Oxford University Press, 2004, Vol 18, Pages 404-406

A Quiet Afternoon in the Cloud Cuckoo Valley
Fans of Rowland Emett will be pleased to know that his fully-working kinetic sculpture, *A Quiet Afternoon in the Cloud Cuckoo Valley*, has been bought by the National Railway Museum in York with help from arts sponsorship. It will be housed in a brand new building, which should be finished by 2024. In the meantime, it will go to Locomotion, the railway museum in Shildon, County Durham, during this year and then, next spring, to the Science and Industry Museum in Manchester.

Emett considered *A Quiet Afternoon in the Cloud Cuckoo Valley* to be his finest work. At 26-foot long, and comprising eight separate automata, it was certainly his largest. Though initially commissioned for a shopping centre, it was no longer needed by the time that it was completed in the mid 1980s. Instead, it was bought and exhibited at Spitalfields in London in 1992. Later put in storage, it narrowly missed being scrapped before it was restored and put on show at Birmingham Museum and Art Gallery in 2014.

143 SMUGGLERS COVE (opposite)
Signed
Pen ink and watercolour
9 x 10 ¾ inches
Illustrated: *Punch*, 30 September 1942, Page 274

144 ... COMING OVER TO ENTERTAIN THE AMERICAN
TROOPS, OR SOMETHING ...
Signed
Pen and ink
10 x 12 ½ inches
Illustrated: *Punch*, 22 September 1943, Page 246;
Sidings, & Suchlike. explored by Emett, London: Faber & Faber, 1946 [unpaginated]; *Alarms & Excursions & Other Transports Transfixed by Emett*, London:
John Murray, 1977, [unpaginated]

146 ... AND WHEN 'E GETS THERE I SUPPOSE THEY'LL CALL
'IM A DESERT RAT
Signed
Pen ink and watercolour
10 ¼ x 12 inches
Illustrated: *Punch*, 3 November 1943, Page 380

145 TAKES A BIT OF GETTING USED TO, A SPOT OF 'OLIDAY
TRAFFIC
Signed
Pen ink and watercolour
12 x 9 ¾ inches
Illustrated: *Punch*, 22 May 1944, Summer Number, [unpaginated];
Sidings, and Suchlike. explored by Emett, London: Faber & Faber, 1946
[unpaginated]; *The Early Morning Milk Train. The Cream of Emett Railway
Drawings*, London: John Murray, 1976 [unpaginated]

147 ... SOMETHING TO DO WITH LEASE-LEND, I EXPECT ...
(opposite)
Signed
Pen ink and watercolour
9 ¼ x 10 ½ inches
Illustrated: *Punch*, 31 March 1943, Page 262;
Sidings, & Suchlike. explored by Emett, London: Faber & Faber, 1946
[unpaginated]; *The Early Morning Milk Train. The Cream of Emett Railway
Drawings*, London: John Murray, 1976 [unpaginated]

148 WELL MET BY LAMP LIGHT
A PLEASANT INTERNATIONAL ENCOUNTER AT CHRISTMASTIDE, SHOWING
A SANTA CLAUS FROM THE OLD COUNTRY CORDIALLY GREETING HIS
COUNTERPART FROM THE NEW WORLD
Signed
Pen ink and watercolour on board
8 ½ x 11 inches

149 PSST ... SQUATTERS IN NUMBER THREE
Signed and inscribed with title and (retrospectively) 'Punch 1947'
Pen and ink
9 ½ x 11 ½ inches
Illustrated: *Punch*, 18 September 1946, Page 222

150 THE PALACE
OF CULTURE III
THE HOTHOUSE OF
BRITISH HUMOUR
Signed
Pen ink and watercolour
17 x 13 inches
Illustrated: *Punch Festival*,
30 April 1951, 'Part I – The
Bouverie Street Exhibition'

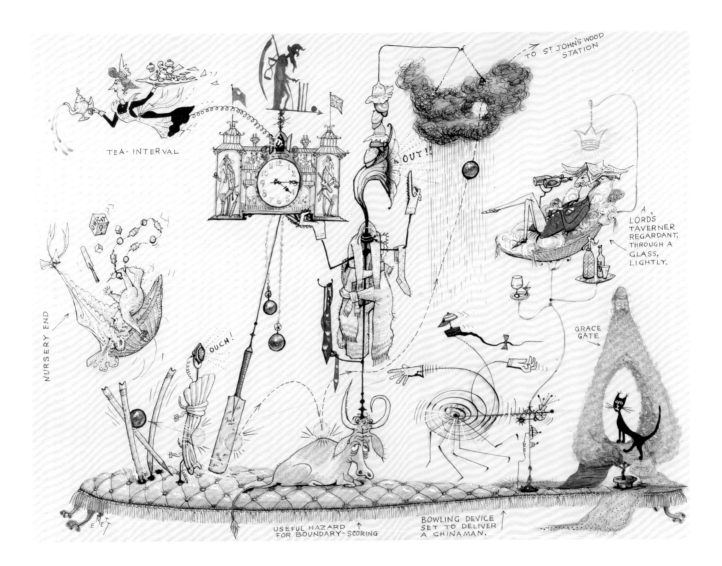

151 A NOSTALGIC APPLICANCE DESIGNED ESPECIALLY FOR
LORD'S TAVERNERS, NOT TO SUPPLANT HAND-CRICKET, BUT
RATHER TO KEEP ALIVE FOND MEMORIES DURING BLIZZARDS,
CHRISTMAS HOLIDAYS AND SUCHLIKE CLOSE SEASONS
Signed
Inscribed with title on original mount
Pen ink and watercolour with bodycolour on board
11 ½ x 15 ½ inches

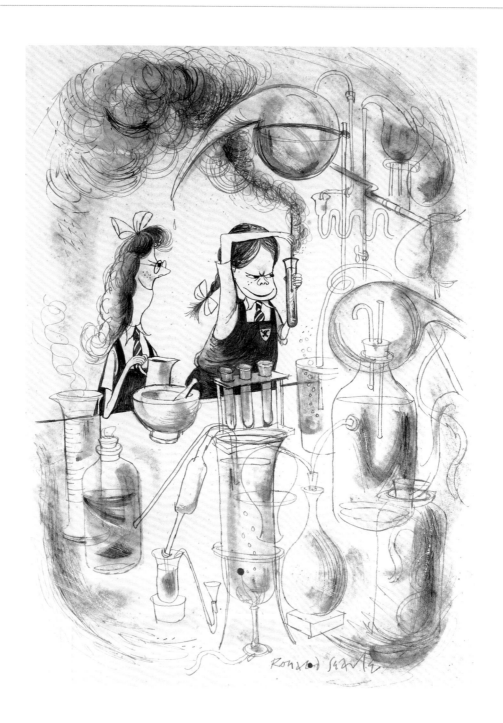

The Increasing Fame of St Trinian's

Originally appearing in *Lilliput* from 1941, Ronald Searle's cartoons about St Trinian's girls' school were gathered by Macdonald & Co in mixed collections of cartoons, beginning with *Hurrah for St Trinian's! and Other Lapses* (1948). Though Searle began to tire of his creation by 1951, a year later he allowed his *News Chronicle* colleague, 'Timothy Shy' (D B Wyndham Lewis), to write a narrative about the school, and illustrated the resulting comic romance, *The Terror of St Trinian's*. The great success of this *jeu d'esprit* – published by Max Parrish – was fuelled by a publicity stunt in which a group of young women, dressed as schoolgirls, invaded Foyle's bookshop. From that point, Searle attempted to bring his involvement with St Trinian's to an end, even publishing *Souls in Torment* (1953) as 'a funeral rite' (Russell Davies, Page 101). However, once Frank Launder and Sidney Gilliatt were allowed to produce a film inspired by Searle's drawings, in 1954, St Trinian's developed a life of its own, making it impossible to quash. Starring George Cole, Joyce Grenfell and Alastair Sim, *The Belles of St Trinian's* immediately entered the popular imagination and, for many people, remains the point of entry to exploring the best-known girls' school in the world. Furthermore, Searle was directly involved in the film and its three most immediate sequels, providing drawings for their title sequences and designing posters to advertise them.

RONALD SEARLE
Ronald William Fordham Searle, CBE (1920-2011)

Equally inspired by a wide range of experience and a great knowledge of the history of caricature, Ronald Searle honed an incisive graphic skill to develop an unparalleled graphic oeuvre, an oeuvre that has made him one of the most popular and influential cartoonist-illustrators.

For a biography of Ronald Searle, please refer to *The Illustrators*, 2018, Page 94.

For essays on various aspects of Ronald Searle's achievement, see *The Illustrators*, 1999, Pages 228-230; and *The Illustrators*, 2000, Pages 40-42.

His work is represented in numerous public collections, including the British Museum and the V&A; and the Bibliothèque Nationale (Paris).

Further reading:
Mark Bryant, 'Searle, Ronald William Fordham (1920-2011)', *Oxford Dictionary of National Biography*, Oxford University Press, May 2015, online

152 OK – NOW PASS THE BAT'S BLOOD (opposite)
Signed and inscribed with title
Inscribed 'Lilliput' below mount
Pen and ink
11 x 7 ½ inches
Illustrated: *Lilliput: The Magazine of Fantasy and Science Fiction*, July 1955, Page 89
Ronald Searle, *The Terror of St Trinian's and Other Drawings*, London: Penguin Books, 2006, as 'Smashing! – Now Pass the Bat's Blood'

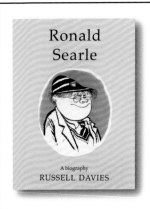 

Russell Davies, *Ronald Searle*, London: Chris Beetles Ltd, 2003. In this new edition of the 1990 hardback biography, Russell Davies and Ronald Searle have added corrections and brought up to date the exhibitions list and bibliography.

Chris Beetles Gallery held the major tribute exhibition, 'Ronald Searle Remembered', in May-June 2012. It was accompanied by a 200 page fully illustrated paperback catalogue, containing newly researched essays and notes.

NORMAN THELWELL
Norman Thelwell (1923-2004)

Norman Thelwell is arguably the most popular cartoonist to have worked in Britain since the Second World War. Though almost synonymous with his immortal subject of little girls and their fat ponies, his work is far more wide ranging, perceptive – and indeed prescient – than that association suggests.

For a biography of Norman Thelwell, please refer to *The Illustrators*, 2009, Page 25.

Having mounted major exhibitions of the work of Thelwell in 1989 and 1991, Chris Beetles encouraged further interest in the artist in 2009 with 'The Definitive Thelwell' and its accompanying catalogue.

The 100-page catalogue surveys all aspects of his career, through 177 illustrations, an appreciation, a biographical chronology and a full bibliography

153 BEGINNER'S LUCK
Signed
Watercolour with pen ink and bodycolour
7 ¾ x 7 ¼ inches

154 EASY COME – EASY GO
Signed
Pen ink and watercolour with bodycolour
11 ½ x 17 ¼ inches
Illustrated: Similar to *Thelwell's Sporting
Prints*, London: Methuen, 1984,
'Easy Come – Easy Go'

GERARD HOFFNUNG
Gerard Hoffnung (1925-1959)

Gerard Hoffnung developed a unique vein of gentle, yet powerful humour through drawings, lectures and even concerts – for his favourite subject was music at its most delightful and daft.

For a biography of Gerard Hoffnung, please refer to *The Illustrators*, 2011, page 257.

Further reading:

Annetta Hoffnung, *Gerard Hoffnung*, London: Gordon Fraser, 1988; Richard Ingrams (rev), 'Hoffnung, Gerard [formerly Gerhardt] (1925-1959)', H C G Matthew and Brian Harrison (eds), *Oxford Dictionary of National Biography*, Oxford University Press, 2004, Vol 27, Pages 523-524

155 DID I NEED BUILDING UP?
Signed
Pen and ink
5 ½ x 8 inches
Illustrated: James Broughton and Gerard Hoffnung, *The Right Playmate*, London: Rupert Hart-Davis, 1952, Page 54

JOHN GLASHAN
John Glashan (1927-1999)

John Glashan was best known as the creator of the cartoon strip, 'Genius', which developed a cult following during its five-year run in the *Observer*. His passion for fine watercolour painting allowed him to develop his world of tiny figures inhabiting beautiful, vast, baroque interiors and sweeping landscapes.

For a biography of John Glashan, please refer to *The Illustrators*, 2017, Page 216.

156 MARCHING FOR NOTHING
Signed
Watercolour
13 ¾ x 10 ¼ inches
Illustrated: *Punch*, 28 September 1996,
Page 6

157 I'M AFRAID WE CAN'T ACCEPT YOU FOR THE POST OF PHYSICAL TRAINING INSTRUCTOR AS YOUR EYES ARE NOT NEAR ENOUGH THE TOP OF YOUR HEAD
Signed and inscribed with title
Watercolour with bodycolour
13 ¼ x 10 ½ inches
Illustrated: *Punch*, 21 September 1996, Page 6

158 'SHAME ON YOU, FEEDING THOSE DUCKS WITH WHITE BREAD, IT'S LACKING IN THE ESSENTIAL NUTRIENTS.'
'THEY ARE NOT REAL DUCKS, THEY ARE PLASTIC DUCKS. THE REAL DUCKS DIED OF MALNUTRITION BECAUSE PEOPLE WERE FEEDING THEM WITH WHITE BREAD.'
Signed
Watercolour and bodycolour
13 x 10 inches
Drawn for *Punch*, circa 1996

Ugh is not feeling very well.

He's been mixing his stagnant waters.

159 'UGH IS NOT FEELING VERY WELL.' 'HE'S BEEN MIXING HIS STAGNANT WATERS.'
Signed and inscribed with title
Watercolour with bodycolour
13 ½ x 10 inches
Illustrated: *Punch*, 5 October 1996, Page 7

160 OWNERS AND
THEIR DOGS
Signed
Watercolour and bodycolour
15 x 11 inches
Illustrated: *Punch*, 19 October
1996, Front Cover

By the way, Dillings, There's a power saw behind The Tool-shed.

161 BY THE WAY, DILLINGS, THERE'S A POWER SAW BEHIND THE TOOL-SHED
Signed and inscribed with title
Watercolour with bodycolour
12 ¾ x 10 inches
Illustrated: *Punch*, 18 January 1997, Page 27

162 I'VE BROUGHT YOU
AN ASHTRAY, SIR
Signed and inscribed with title
Watercolour with bodycolour
13 x 9 ½ inches
Illustrated: *Punch*, 4 January 1997,
Page 45

LARRY

Terence Parkes (1927-2003), known as 'Larry'

Larry was the cartoonist's cartoonist, highly respected by his peers for his consistently funny work, and cherished by them for his affability. In the autobiographical *Larry on Larry* (1994), he wrote, 'I seem to have the reputation for a being a beer-swigging Brummie cartoonist', and while each particular of that statement may have been true, its overall spirit suggests an essential modesty. He even expressed some reservations about the increasing seriousness with which cartooning was being taken, and yet was steeped in the history of his profession and, more widely, in the history of art. This combination of the easygoing and the erudite informed much of his work, in content and draughtsmanship, and he will long be remembered for both his frequent depiction of an Everyman figure, 'Larry's man', and his parodies of famous works of art.

For a biography of Larry, please refer to *The Illustrators*, 2014, page 226.

His work is represented in the collections of the British Museum and the V&A; and the British Cartoon Archive, University of Kent (Canterbury), and the University of Essex.

163 RODIN'S THE SMOKERS
Signed
Pen ink and watercolour
7 ½ x 8 ¼ inches
Exhibited: 'The Humour Show', Nunnington Hall, March-April 2016

164 DID YOU HAVE A GOOD ROUND MONSIEUR COURBET?
Pen ink and watercolour
7 ½ x 10 ¾ inches
Exhibited: 'Hole in One!', The Atkinson Gallery Southport, May-August 2017

165 WALT DISNEY IN HIS STUDIO
(opposite)
Pen ink and watercolour
13 x 16 inches

WALT DISNEY IN HIS STUDIO

166 HENRI ROUSSEAU –
VISIT TO BRITAIN 1907
Signed and inscribed with title
Watercolour and bodycolour
6 ½ x 9 inches

167 THE ANAESTHETICS
LESSON OF DR TULIP
Signed
Pen ink and watercolour
7 ¼ x 10 ¼ inches

MARK BOXER

Charles Mark Edward Boxer (1931-1988), known as
'Marc' and 'Mark Boxer'

As one of the greatest caricaturists of the twentieth-
century, Mark Boxer satirised the country's social
elite – a world of beautiful, fashionable, metropolitan
figures which he himself was very much a part. Equally
adept as a social cartoonist, he effectively captured the
lives of the upper-middle classes, continuing this great
tradition from the likes of Pont and Osbert Lancaster.

For a biography of Mark Boxer, please refer to *The Illustrators*,
2017, Page 226.

His work is represented in the collections of the National
Portrait Gallery.

Further reading:
Mark Amory (rev), 'Boxer, (Charles) Mark Edward [*pseud* Marc]
(1931-1988)', H C G Matthew and Brian Harrison (eds), *Oxford Dictionary of
National Biography*, Oxford University Press, 2004, Vol 7, Pages 8-9

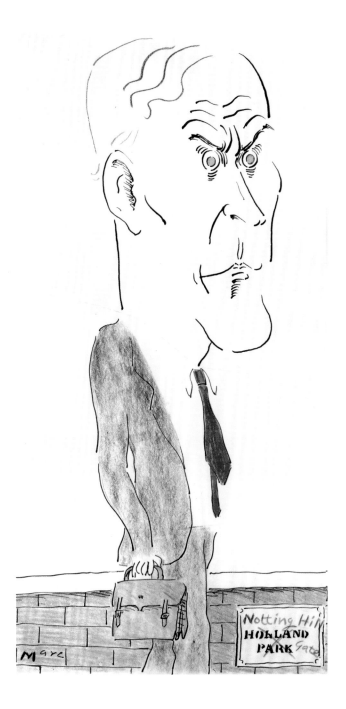

168 TONY BENN
Signed
Pen ink and coloured pencil
13 ¼ x 8 ¼ inches

169 ENOCH POWELL
Signed
Inscribed with title and dated 1984 below mount
Pen and ink
9 x 7 ¾ inches
Similar to Mark Bryant, *Dictionary of Twentieth-Century British Cartoonists and Caricaturists*, Aldershot: Ashgate Publishing, 2000, Front Cover & Page 33

170 JEREMY THORPE
Signed
Pen and ink with pencil
10 ½ x 7 inches

171 RUPERT MURDOCH
Signed
Pen and ink
10 ¼ x 8 ¼ inches

172 WARREN BEATTY AND JACK NICHOLSON IN REDS
Signed and inscribed with title
Pen and ink
11 ¼ x 8 ¼ inches

173 HOW CLEVER OF THEM TO FIND SOMEBODY HE HASN'T BEEN OUT WITH
Signed
Pen and ink
6 ¼ x 3 ½ inches

174 WE CAN'T ASK THEM, SIMON; THEY'RE RIGHT OF MODERATE ...
Signed
Pen and ink
8 x 3 ¾ inches

175 WHAT IS THE POINT IN LIVING WITH SOMEONE IF ONE STILL HAS TO HAVE THEIR MOTHER FOR CHRISTMAS?
Signed
Pen and ink
7 ¾ x 3 ¾ inches
Illustrated: *The Times*

176 I'M HAVING TO CHAPERONE MUMMY TO THE STONES CONCERT ...
Signed
Pen and ink
8 x 3 ½ inches
Illustrated: *The Times*

ROY GERRARD

Roy Gerrard (1935-1997)

Roy Gerrard was best known for his delightful picture books, which 'charmed children with ... bouncy rhymes and thumb-shaped characters acting out their adventures – and misadventures – in sumptuous period settings' (Wolfgang Saxon, *The New York Times*, 13 August 1997, Obituary).

For a biography of Roy Gerrard, please refer to *The Ilustrators*, 2015, page 246.

Detail of **177**

177 SUNDAY
MORNING (below)
Signed
Inscribed with title and 'water
colour' below mount
Watercolour
7 ¾ x 17 ½ inches

178 THE OVERHEAD
SMASH (opposite)
Inscribed with title and 'water
colour' below mount
Watercolour with pen and ink
12 x 9 ½ inches

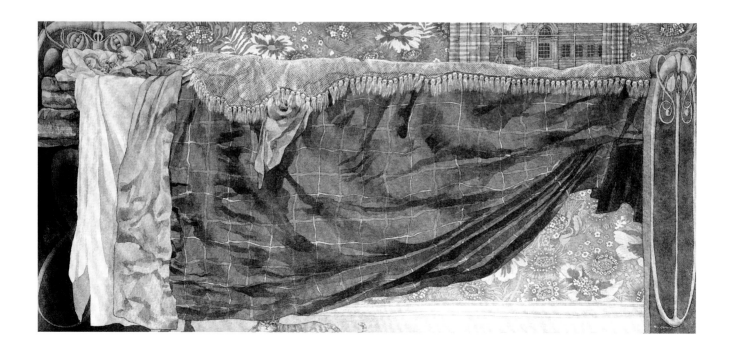

The King and Queen were overjoyed
   to see their sweet Matilda.
They thought by now Black Ned had either
      married her or killed her.
They thanked Sir Cedric gratefully
   and said that he must stay
To keep Matilda company
   and have a holiday.

180 THE KING AND HIS QUEEN WERE DELIGHTED, AND READILY GAVE THEIR CONSENT.
THE HELD A GREAT FEAST AND TOLD ALL THEIR FRIENDS OF THE FORTH-COMING HAPPY EVENT
Signed
Watercolour
4 x 8 ½ inches

Nos **179-182** are all from the
Estate of Leo and Jane McKern,
and are illustrated in Roy Gerrard,
Sir Cedric, London: Victor
Gollancz, 1984, [unpaginated]

Nos **180-182** were all exhibited
at the National Theatre, 1984, as
'The Banquet'

Nos **179** and **180** are both sold
with autograph letters of thanks
from Roy Gerrard to Leo McKern,
dated October 1984, on paper
headed with the artist's address

179 THE KING AND QUEEN WERE OVERJOYED
TO SEE THEIR SWEET MATILDA.
THEY THOUGHT BY NOW BLACK NED HAD EITHER
MARRIED HER OR KILLED HER.
THEY THANKED SIR CEDRIC GRATEFULLY
AND SAID THAT HE MUST STAY
TO KEEP MATILDA COMPANY
AND HAVE A HOLIDAY
(opposite above)
Signed
Watercolour with pen and ink
10 x 18 ¼ inches
Exhibited: National Theatre, 1984,
as 'The Joyful Return'

181 THE BANQUET [I]
(above)
Signed
Watercolour
4 x 8 ½ inches

182 THE BANQUET [II]
(below)
Signed
Watercolour
4 x 8 ½ inches

WALT DISNEY
Walt Disney Studio (founded in 1923)

For an essay on the Walt Disney Studio, please refer to
The Illustrators, 1999, Pages 206-209

183 BAMBI AND FLOWER
Signed and inscribed 'To James Irwin with best wishes'
by Walt Disney on original mount
Hand painted cel on courvoisier background
6 ½ inches circular
Provenance: Courvoisier Galleries,
San Francisco, California

This hand-painted cel was produced for Walt Disney's *Bambi* (1942), and is
dedicated to the NASA astronaut, James Irwin.

Walt Disney was fascinated by space travel and in 1965 visited Marshall Space Flight
Center in Huntsville, Alabama, where he possibly met James Irwin for the first time.
Irwin would walk on the moon as part of the Apollo 15 mission in 1971. He became
the first official rider of Space Mountain when it opened at Disneyland in Anaheim,
California, in 1975.

Walt Disney's signature has been verified by Howard Lowery.

CHARLES SCHULZ
Charles Monroe Schulz (1922-2000)

Charles Schulz was the creator of 'Peanuts', one of the most influential and universally loved of comic strips. The central character of the strip's cast of children is purportedly the eternal loser Charlie Brown, though he is constantly upstaged by his pet dog, the popular Snoopy. It has been best known in Britain through appearances in the *Daily Mail* and as an animated television series.

The only child of a barber, Charles Schulz was born in Minneapolis, Minnesota, on 26 November 1922. He grew up mainly in St Paul, where he attended various schools, including the Central High School. He was there encouraged in his drawing skills by his art teacher, Minette Paro, and, in spring 1940, enrolled in a correspondence course with the Bureau of Engraving at Minneapolis, which placed an emphasis on cartooning. Serving in Europe with the United States Army during the Second World War, he then joined the Bureau of Engraving as an instructor. At the same time, he began to provide lettering for the work of other cartoonists, and then, from February 1947, worked as a cartoonist in his own right.

The genesis of 'Peanuts' began in June 1947, when Schulz contributed two cartoons entitled 'Sparky's Li'l Folks' to the *Minneapolis Tribune*. 'Li'l Folks' soon began to appear on a weekly basis in the other major local newspaper, the *St Paul Pioneer Press*. Three years later, he achieved a syndication contract for 'Li'l Folks' with United Feature Syndicate. However, the syndicate decided to change its title to 'Peanuts' in order to avoid confusion with an earlier strip called 'Little Folks'. It then appeared six days a week in seven newspapers nationwide. From 1952, most newspapers also ran a full colour 'Peanuts' strip on a Sunday. The success of 'Peanuts' led to the publication, from 1952 to 1964, of 'Peanuts' comic books, and to merchandising, advertising, animations and dramatisations. The recipient of many awards, Schulz continued to write and draw the 'Peanuts' strip into the 1990s. He died at home, at Santa Rosa, California, on 12 February 2000. Twice married, he had four children with his first wife.

Further reading

Ann T Keene, 'Schulz, Charles M (26 Nov 1922-12 Feb 2000)', Paul Betz and Mark C Carnes (eds), *American National Biography*, Oxford University Press, 2002, supplement 1, Pages 549-550

184 YOU COULD WRITE A WHOLE NOVEL ABOUT MY LIFE
Signed 'Schulz' and 'Charles M Schulz', inscribed 'best wishes'
and dated 1-24
Pen and ink with zippatone
6 ¼ x 19 ¾ inches
Illustrated: Syndicated across United States newspapers on 24 January 1995

PETER ARNO

Curtis Arnoux Peters Jr,
known as 'Peter Arno'
(1904-1968)

Hailed as 'the greatest artist in the
world' by its founder Harold Ross,
Peter Arno did much to establish
The New Yorker's reputation for
sophisticated humour, through his
satirical look at the decadent New
York society of the inter-war period.
Quickly establishing himself as one
of the pillars of the magazine's
earliest days, Peter Arno would
continue to produce cartoons and
covers for *The New Yorker* until his
death, an association of over 40
years. Described as 'a master of
composition', perhaps his most
famous cartoon, which he produced
in 1941, coined the phrase 'back to
the old drawing board'.

For a biography of Peter Arno, please
refer to *The Illustrators*, 2016, Page 93.

Further reading
Robert C Harvey, 'Arno, Peter (8 Jan 1904-22
Feb 1968)', John A Garraty and Mark C Carnes
(eds), *American National Biography*, Oxford
University Press, 1999, Vol 1, Pages 628-629

185 YOU BOYS CARE FOR A
LITTLE FUN?
Signed
Pen ink and watercolour
14 ¾ x 11 ¾ inches
Illustrated: *The New Yorker*, 22 October
1932, Page 21
Exhibited: The Leicester Galleries,
London, December 1932, No 89

WHITNEY DARROW
Whitney Darrow Jr (1909-1999)

Whitney Darrow was a fluent, masterly draughtsman, who is best known for many gently satiric cartoons for *The New Yorker*, and especially those that focus on aspects of middle-class suburban life. Unusually among its contributors, he also wrote his own witty captions.

Whitney Darrow was born in Princeton, New Jersey, on 22 August 1909, the son of Charles Whitney Darrow, a founding director of Princeton University Press, and May Temperance (née Barton). Growing up in Greenwich, Connecticut, he was educated at Greenwich High School and then Princeton University, where he majored in History. While at Princeton, he contributed parodies to the *Daily Princetonian* and took up the position of art editor for the *Princeton Tiger*. Following graduation in 1931, he spent his evenings painting at the Art Students' League of New York, under Thomas Hart Benton, and his days drawing cartoons for several magazines, including *Ballyyoo*, *Judge* and *Town Tidings*. At the age of 24, in 1933, he sold his first cartoon to *The New Yorker*, and soon became one of the most prolific cartoonist contributors, contributing 50 images a year, and the occasional cover. Many of these were republished in four collections, beginning with *You're Sitting On My Eyelashes* (1943).

"I want you to draw up a petition in bankruptcy."

186 I WANT YOU TO DRAW UP A PETITION IN BANKRUPTCY
Signed and inscribed with title
Charcoal
13 ½ x 11 ¼ inches
Illustrated: *The New Yorker*, 12 September 1964, Page 43

In 1938, Darrow married the artist, Betty Waldo Parish, whom he probably met at the Art Students' League, and who became best known as a printmaker. However, their marriage was not a success and, in 1942, he married Mildred Lois Adkins. Together they would have a son, Whitney Barton, and a daughter, Linda Ann.

From the 1950s, Darrow worked increasingly as an illustrator, developing something of a speciality in drawing children, for books aimed at a range of readerships, both old and young. So he illustrated such adult titles as B M Attkinson's *What Dr Spock Didn't Tell Us* (1959) and Louise Armstrong's *A Child's Guide to Freud* (1963), and produced the images for such picture books as Robert Kraus's *Unidentified Flying Elephant* (1968) and his own, *I'm Glad I'm a Boy! I'm Glad I'm a Girl!* (1970). However, the last, which has been described as 'the most sexist book ever', is likely to have been satirical in intention, in undermining gender stereotypes, and so aimed at adults.

Darrow retired from *The New Yorker* in 1982, having published more than 1,500 cartoons in the magazine. He lived latterly in Shelburne, Vermont, and died in hospital in Burlington, Vermont, on 10 August 1999.

His work is represented in the collections of Princeton University Library, NJ.

187 A FUNNY THING HAPPENED ON THE WAY TO THE FORUM
Signed
Pencil and charcoal
11 x 9 inches
Exhibited: 'The Americans Are Coming',
Chris Beetles Gallery, May 2015

DAVID LEVINE

David Julian Levine (1926-2009)

David Levine was widely acknowledged as one of the greatest, and most influential, caricaturists of the second half of the twentieth century. Best known as the staff artist of *The New York Review of Books*, he revived the tradition of American political caricature that originated in the nineteenth century with Thomas Nast, and has been frequently described as equal to Honoré Daumier. However, he sustained an equally distinguished career as a painter, producing figurative oils and watercolours in a poetically naturalistic style. His love of Corot and Vuillard, Eakins and Sargent, pervades his studies of Coney Island and the Garment District. But more fundamental to both his paintings and his caricatures is the fact that he said, 'I love my species'.

For a biography of David Levine, please refer to *The Illustrators*, 2010, pages 277-278.

His work is represented in numerous public collections, including the National Portrait Gallery; and Brooklyn Museum, the Cleveland Museum of Art, the Library of Congress (Washington DC), the Metropolitan Museum of Art (New York), the National Portrait Gallery (Smithsonian Institution, Washington DC) and The Morgan Library & Museum (New York).

Further reading (including collections of caricatures)
Thomas S Buechner (foreword), *The Arts of David Levine*, New York: Alfred A Knopf, 1978; Thomas S Buechner, *Paintings and Drawings by David Levine and Aaron Shikler*, New York: Brooklyn Institute of Arts and Sciences, 1971; John Kenneth Galbraith (intro), *No Known Survivors. David Levine's Political Prank*, Boston: Gambit, 1970; David Leopold (ed), *American Presidents*, Seattle: Fantagraphics, 2008; Malcolm Muggeridge (intro), *The Man from M.A.L.I.C.E.*, New York: Dutton, 1960; John Updike (intro), *Pens and Needles. Literary Caricatures by David Levine*, Boston: Gambit, 1969; Ian McKibbin White, *The Watercolors of David Levine*, Washington DC: The Phillips Collection, 1980

188 HERBERT MARCUSE
Signed and dated 68
Inscribed 'books' below mount
5 x 5 inches

189 ROSSINI
Signed and dated 68
Inscribed 'recording' below mount
Pen and ink
5 ½ x 5 inches

190 FRED ASTAIRE
Signed and dated 73
Pen and ink on paper laid on board
7 ½ x 9 ½ inches
Illustrated: *The New York Review of Books*, 29 November 1973, 'Movie Crazy' by
Michael Wood (a review of several books about films, including *The Fred Astaire
and Ginger Rogers Book* by Arlene Croce)

EDWARD KOREN
Edward Benjamin Koren (born 1935)

Edward Koren is undoubtedly one of the most loved and revered cartoonists in the history of *The New Yorker*. With his first cartoon appearing in 1962, he has since produced over one thousand cartoons, illustrations and covers for the magazine. Famous for his wonderfully fuzzy beasts, Koren delights in making, in his own words, 'the ordinary and mundane hairy and unshorn'.

For a biography of Edward Koren, please refer to *The Illustrators*, 2015, Page 170.

191 BEFORE WE CUT THE CAKE, I WANT TO THANK MY BRIDE FOR BRINGING OUR WEDDING IN UNDER BUDGET
Signed
Inscribed with title and publication details and dated 5-2-14 on reverse
Pen and ink
21 x 19 ½ inches
Illustrated: *The New Yorker*, 8 September 2014, Page 67

192 HEY – WE JUST CATCH AND RELEASE
(opposite)
Signed
Inscribed with title and publication details and
dated 1-26-16 on reverse
Pen and ink
21 x 23 inches
Illustrated: *The New Yorker*, 11 April 2016, Page 69

193 PETER, AS YOU GET OLDER
YOU GET TO BE MORE FUN
Signed and inscribed with title
Pen and ink
9 ¾ x 14 inches

194 LET US DRINK TO EVEN
MORE PATERNALISM
Signed and inscribed with title
Pen and ink
12 ¼ x 14 inches

JOHN BURNINGHAM
John Mackintosh Burningham (1936-2019)

John Burningham was arguably the greatest British creator of picture books since the Second World War, with an oeuvre that ranges from *Borka* (1963) through *Mr Gumpy's Outing* (1970) to late achievements that include *Motor Miles* (2015) and *Mouse House* (2017). Popular with all ages, he sometimes aimed a subject particularly at adults, as with *John Burningham's Champagne* (2015).

For a biography of John Burningham, please refer to *The Illustrators*, 2018, Page 117.

In December 2016, the Chris Beetles Gallery mounted a major selling retrospective of work by John Burningham. It was accompanied by a fully illustrated catalogue, which includes a comprehensive bibliography.

195, **196**, **199-206** were all exhibited in 'John Burningham. An illustrator for all ages', Chris Beetles Gallery, December 2016-January 2017

195-197 were drawn for but not illustrated in John Burningham, *Would You Rather ...*, London: Jonathan Cape, 1978, [unpaginated]

**1978 –
Would You Rather ...**

195 WOULD YOU RATHER ... DRIVE A BULLDOZER
Signed
Watercolour of pigs on reverse
Pen ink, watercolour, spraypaint, crayon and pencil
13 ¼ x 21 ¼ inches

197 WOULD YOU RATHER BE ... SQUASHED BY A HIPPO
Signed and inscribed with title and 'rolled on'
Inscribed 'change to rhino?' below mount
Pen ink, watercolour and pencil, 5 x 8 ¼ inches

196 MASHED WORMS
Signed
Pen ink, watercolour and
bodycolour
5 ¾ x 4 inches

198 SWALLOWED BY A
FISH
Pen ink, watercolour and pencil
6 x 9 ½ inches
Preliminary drawing for John
Burningham, *Would You Rather ...*,
London: Harper Collins
Children's Books, 1978,
[unpaginated]
Exhibited: 'Alive! Contemporary
British Illustration', Myles Meehan
Gallery, Dartington Arts Centre,
September-November 2010

1985 – John Burningham's ABC

199-204 are all illustrated in *John Burningham's ABC* [Play and Learn Series], London: Walker Books, 1985, [unpaginated]

199 COW
Signed
Pen ink, watercolour and pencil
6 x 6 inches

200 KANGAROO
Signed
Pen and ink drawing of a boy holding flowers on reverse
Pen ink, watercolour, coloured pencil and pencil
9 ½ x 7 inches

201 LIZARD
Signed
Pen ink, watercolour and coloured pencil
5 x 9 ½ inches

202 SNAKE
Signed
Pen ink and coloured pencil
4 x 6 ½ inches

203 ZEBRA
Signed
Pen ink, watercolour and
coloured pencil with pencil
4 ½ x 6 ¼ inches

204 PARROT
Signed
Pen ink, watercolour and crayon
with pencil
9 x 6 inches

205 'I WANT TO BE WITH MY MOTHER AND FATHER AGAIN,'
SAID ALBERT.
THE QUEEN FELT SORRY FOR ALBERT AND SHE THOUGHT
FOR A LONG TIME
Signed
Pen ink, watercolour, coloured pencil and pencil on collaged paper on a
photographic base overlaid with spraypaint and bodycolour on celluloid
13 x 19 ¼ inches
Illustrated: John Burningham, *Cloudland*, London: Jonathan Cape,
1996, [unpaginated]

206 GOING TO A PARTY
Signed
Pen ink, watercolour and pencil
8 x 11 inches
Drawn for but not illustrated in John Burningham, *It's a Secret*,
London: Walker Books, 2009, [unpaginated]

MICHAEL FOREMAN
Michael Foreman, RDI (born 1938)

1978/2012 – Popular Folk Tales

While Michael Foreman is perhaps best
known as one of the most outstanding
contemporary creators of children's books,
he is a wide-ranging artist, illustrating
literary classics and working as a painter.

For a biography of Michael Foreman, please
refer to *The Illustrators*, 2018, Pages 132-133.

His work is represented in the collections of
the V&A.

Further reading
'Michael Foreman', in Douglas Martin, *The Telling Line*,
London: Julia MacRae Books, 1989, Pages 291-311

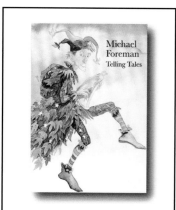

Michael Foreman: *Telling Tales*, London:
Chris Beetles Ltd, 2017. Fully illustrated
catalogue, paperback, 140 pages

207 FETCHING DOWN THE MOON
Signed, inscribed with 'The Moon' and
'The Brothers Grimm', and dated '78
Watercolour with pencil
10 ¾ x 7 ¼ inches
Illustrated: The Brothers Grimm (tr Brian
Alderson), *Popular Folk Tales*, Dorking:
Templar Publishing, 2012, Page 91

1981 – Fairy Tales

208 TERRY JONES FAIRY
TALES BACK COVER
Inscribed '"Terry Jones Fairy
Tales" cover'
Watercolour with bodycolour
and pencil
11 ½ x 8 ¼ inches
Illustrated: Terry Jones, *Fairy
Tales*, London: Pavilion Books,
1981, Back Cover

209 TERRY JONES FAIRY
TALES FRONT COVER
Signed twice and dated '81
Watercolour with pencil
11 ½ x 9 ¼ inches
Illustrated: Terry Jones, *Fairy
Tales*, London, Pavilion Books,
1981, Front Cover

1981 – Panda and the Odd Lion

210 PANDA AND THE ODD LION
Signed twice
Signed and inscribed with book title on reverse
Watercolour with ink and pencil
9 ¾ x 16 ¼ inches
Drawn for but not illustrated in Michael Foreman, *Panda and the Odd Lion*, London: Hamish Hamilton, 1981

211 PANDA AND THE ODD LION MEET THE PLATYPUS
Signed twice
Signed and inscribed with book title on reverse
Watercolour with ink and pencil
9 ¾ x 16 ¼ inches
Drawn for but not illustrated in Michael Foreman, *Panda and the Odd Lion*, London: Hamish Hamilton, 1981

1982 – Land of Dreams

212 THEY WOULD PUSH AND PULL THEM INTO THEIR
VALLEY, WHICH BECAME A VAST STORE OF BITS AND PIECES.
A SCRAPYARD OF DREAMS
Signed, inscribed with book title and dated 1982
Watercolour with bodycolour and pencil
11 ½ x 18 ¾ inches
Illustrated: Michael Foreman, *Land of Dreams*, London: Andersen Press,
1982, [unpaginated]

1984 – Cat & Canary

213 DOWN THEY WENT, THROUGH THE SNOW TOWARDS
THE BRIGHT FLASHING LIGHTS OF THE CITY
Signed and inscribed with book title
Watercolour, ink and bodycolour with pencil
10 ¾ x 16 inches
Illustrated: Michael Foreman, *Cat & Canary*, London: Andersen Press, 1984,
[unpaginated]

214 AFTER THE FIRST TERRIBLE FRIGHT, CAT WAS THRILLED
TO BE FLYING FREE AS A BIRD
Signed and dated 1984
Signed, inscribed with book title and dated 1984 on reverse
Watercolour and ink with pencil
10 ¾ x 16 inches
Illustrated: Michael Foreman, *Cat & Canary*, London: Andersen Press, 1984,
[unpaginated]

1988 – The Night Before Christmas

215 THE NIGHT BEFORE CHRISTMAS
Signed, inscribed with title and dated 1988
Watercolour
11 ½ x 24 ¼ inches
Illustrated: Clement Moore, *The Night Before Christmas*,
New York: Viking Kestrel, 1988, Front Cover

1990 – Michael Foreman's World of Fairy Tales

216 POPOCATEPETL
HOLDS THE TORCH IN
MEMORY OF HIS PRINCESS
Signed, inscribed with title and
dated '90
Watercolour and ink with pencil
12 ¼ x 9 inches
Illustrated: Michael Foreman
(Selected), *Michael Foreman's
World of Fairy Tales*, London:
Pavilion Books, 1990, Page 111,
'Popocatepetl and the Princess'
(Mexico)

1998 – Chicken Licken

217 CHICKEN LICKEN
Signed
Inscribed with title and dated 1998 below mount
Watercolour and pastel with pencil
15 ¼ x 23 ¼ inches
Drawn for but not illustrated in Michael Foreman,
Chicken Licken, London: Red Fox Publishing, 1998

218 CAT IN THE MANGER
(opposite)
Signed, inscribed with title and dated 2000
Watercolour with bodycolour
11 ¼ x 12 ½ inches
Drawn for but not illustrated in Michael
Foreman, *Cat in the Manger*, London:
Andersen Press, 2000

2000 – Cat in the Manger

2002 – Toro! Toro!   **2005 – Classic Fairy Tales**

'Toro, Toro'

219 TORO, TORO
Signed and inscribed with title
Watercolour and pencil
4 x 4 ¼ inches
Drawn for but not illustrated in Michael
Morpurgo, *Toro! Toro!*, London: Harper
Collins, 2002

220 A FLOCK OF BEAUTIFUL BIRDS EMERGED
FROM AMONG THE REEDS
Signed and inscribed 'The Ugly Duckling'
Watercolour with pencil
8 ¼ x 6 ¼ inches
Illustrated: Michael Foreman (Reteller), *Classic Fairy Tales*,
London: Chrysalis Children's Books, 2005, Page 65, 'The
Ugly Duckling'

2005 – Can't Catch Me!

221 TICKLE, TICKLE!
Signed, inscribed with title and
dated 2005
Watercolour with pencil
12 ½ x 17 ½ inches
Illustrated: Michael Foreman,
Can't Catch Me!, London:
Andersen Press, 2005,
[unpaginated]

222 HARRUMF!
HARRROOO!
Signed, inscribed with title and
book title, and dated 2005
Watercolour with pencil
12 ½ x 18 ¼ inches
Illustrated: Michael Foreman,
Can't Catch Me!, London:
Andersen Press, 2005,
[unpaginated]

2007 – Soggy the Bear

223 SOGGY THE BEAR
Signed and inscribed with title
Watercolour and pencil
12 x 18 inches
Illustrated: Philip Moran, *Soggy the Bear,*
Saltash: Mabecron Books, 2007, Cover

224 SAVE YOUR TEARS, LITTLE SEA
DRAGON (opposite)
Signed, inscribed with title and dated 2017
Watercolour with pencil
10 ½ x 9 ½ inches
Similar to Helen Dunmore, *The Little Sea Dragon's
Wild Adventure*, Saltash: Mabecron Books, 2017,
page 16

2017 – The Little Sea Dragon's Wild Adventure

2019 – The Mermaid's Christmas Adventure

225-229 are all signed, drawn in watercolour with pencil and bodycolour and illustrated in Michael Foreman, *The Mermaid's Christmas Adventure*, Saltash: Mabecron Books, 2019

225 AS THEY WATCHED, A STRANGE FLYING BOAT APPEARED IN FRONT OF THEIR EYES
11 x 8 ½ inches
Illustrated: *The Mermaid's Christmas Adventure*, Page 14

226 'I KNEW IT,' SAID MER MOTHER. 'IT'S SANTA CLAUS!' (opposite)
11 x 11 ½ inches
Illustrated: *The Mermaid's Christmas Adventure*, Pages 15-16

227 FROM THE AIR IT LOOKED LIKE A FAIRY-LAND, THE HARBOUR GLITTERING WITH COLOURED LIGHTS AND TINSEL DECORATED CHRISTMAS TREES
12 x 16 ½ inches
Illustrated: *The Mermaid's Christmas Adventure*, Pages 16-17

228 THEY WERE A GREAT TEAM TOGETHER AND STOPPED OFF AT ALL THE HOUSES IN THE TOWN AND THEN ZOOMED OFF TO THE NEXT TOWN
11 ½ x 16 ¾ inches
Illustrated: *The Mermaid's Christmas Adventure*, Pages 20-21

229 SANTA WAS BUSY THE WHOLE NIGHT, DISAPPEARING DOWN
CHIMNEY AFTER CHIMNEY, SOMETIMES RETURNING WITH
DELICIOUS FOOD FOR THEM – CALLED MINCE PIES – AND MORE
CARROTS FOR THE TWO REINDEER
11 x 17 inches
Illustrated: *The Mermaid's Christmas Adventure*, Pages 22-23

AMANDA HALL

Amanda Hall (born 1956)

Amanda Hall is an award-winning contemporary illustrator, particularly renowned for her wonderfully decorative and colourful children's book illustrations, as well as her work for educational publications both in Britain and America.

For a biography of Amanda Hall, please refer to *The Illustrators*, 2011, Page 356.

Amanda is just completing *Little Bear*, an Inuit story from Greenland retold by Dawn Casey, which will be published in the USA by Wisdom Tales. She will then work on her next project for Eerdmans Books for Young Readers, a book to be called *How the Sea Came to Be – And all the creatures in it*, written by Jennifer Berne.

230 YOUNG LEONORA
10 ½ x 21 ½ inches
Illustrated: *Out of This World*,
Cover

'*Out of This World* is Amanda Hall's second picture book about the life and work of a significant figure from art history. The first – also written by Michelle Markel – is *The Fantastic Jungles of Henri Rousseau* [2012] … *Out of This World* is the fascinating and stunningly illustrated story of Leonora Carrington, a girl who made art out of her imagination and created some of the most enigmatic and startling works of the last eighty years … From life in Paris creating art alongside Max Ernst to Mexico, where she met Diego Rivera and Frida Kahlo, Leonora's life became intertwined with the powerful events and people that shaped the twentieth century.' (as described on the dustjacket of *Out of This World*)

230-239 are all signed and drawn in watercolour ink, pencil crayon and chalk pastel colouring pencil with bodycolour. They are Illustrated in Michelle Markel, *Out of This World: The Surreal Art of Leonora Carrington*, New York: Balzer + Bray, an imprint of Harper Collins Publishers, 2019, [unpaginated]

231 LEONORA,
THE OWL AND
THE PUSSYCAT
6 ¼ x 8 ¼ inches
Illustrated: *Out of This World*,
Frontispiece

232 PICTURES CAME
FLOODING OUT ...
9 ½ x 20 ½ inches

233 LEONORA WANTED TO PAINT HER OWN IMAGINED WORLDS
8 ½ x 12 ¾ inches

234 IN 1940, GERMANY INVADED WESTERN EUROPE
8 x 12 ¾ inches

235 ... MOST OF THE ARTISTS THERE WERE BOSSY OLD MEN
(opposite)
9 ½ x 10 ½ inches

236 LEONORA BEFRIENDED
A SPANISH ARTIST NAMED
REMEDIOS, WHO LIVED IN
A BROKEN-DOWN
APARTMENT FILLED WITH
CATS, STONES AND
MAGIC CRYSTALS
9 ½ x 10 ¼ inches

237 'COULD YOU
MAKE MORE' HE ASKED.
COULD SHE!
(opposite above)
9 ½ x 20 ¼ inches

238 HER MYSTICAL
PAINTINGS BECAME WELL
KNOWN THROUGHOUT
THE WORLD
(opposite below)
9 ½ x 20 ½ inches

Illustrated as Back Endpaper
in the present catalogue:

239 LEONORA'S WORLD
9 ½ x 20 ½ inches
Illustrated: *Out of This World*,
Endpapers

CAROLINE MAGERL

Caroline Magerl (born 1964)

Caroline Magerl is an award-winning and internationally distinguished illustrator, cartoonist and painter, who is now recognised as a unique and arresting presence. Her work spans from dark, enigmatic oil paintings, through incisive cartoons, to lively children's book illustrations. It has been exhibited in a variety of galleries and art fairs and celebrated in numerous publications.

For a biography of Caroline Magerl, please refer to *The Illustrators*, 2014, Page 307.

Since the artwork for Caroline Magerl's *Maya and Cat* (2018) was included in the last exhibition of 'The Illustrators', the book has been shortlisted for the New South Wales Premier's Literary Award (Patricia Wrightson Prize) and was listed as a Notable Picture Book by the Children's Book Council of Australia. In addition, Caroline has received the support of a fellowship from the May Gibbs Children's Literature Trust.

Caroline's new book, *Nop*, is a heart-warming picture book about a scruffy bear who forges a lasting friendship with another unlikely loner. It will be published by Walker Books in Australia in November 2019 and in the UK in January 2020, and Chris Beetles Gallery will launch the book with an exhibition of the original artwork. The current catalogue provides a foretaste of its many charms.

240-242 are all signed, drawn in pen ink and watercolour, and illustrated in Caroline Magerl, *Nop*, Newtown, NSW: Walker Books Australia, 2019, [unpaginated]

240 NOP WAS NOT PLUSH IN PLACES
(opposite left)
8 x 6 ¼ inches

241 ... FRIEND
(opposite right)
8 ½ x 8 inches

242 SO HE WATCHED THE LITTER TUMBLE
14 ¾ x 12 inches

"Well, **you** have a word with him about queue-jumping."

"Well, this is a waste of time again!"

243 WELL, YOU HAVE A WORD WITH HIM ABOUT
QUEUE-JUMPING
Signed and inscribed with title
Pen ink and watercolour
with bodycolour
15 ¼ × 10 ½ inches
Illustrated: *The Oldie*, 2019

244 WELL, THIS IS A WASTE OF TIME AGAIN!
Signed and dated 9/5/19
Pen ink and watercolour
16 × 12 inches
Redraw of a cartoon that originally appeared in *Punch*

ED MCLACHLAN
Edward Rolland McLachlan (born 1940)

Ed McLachlan's cartoons offer a comical but often cutting commentary on modern life. From his gormless, baggy-suited businessmen to his ungainly bucktoothed women, his undeniably British sense of humour makes him a master of the macabre with an eye for the ridiculous. In every cleverly observed image, he takes the mundane and delivers the hilariously absurd.

For a biography of Ed McLachlan, please refer to *The Illustrators*, 2002, page 110.

His work is represented in the collections of the British Cartoon Archive (University of Kent).

245 THE ONE THING I HATE ABOUT SUMMER – GREAT BIG MOTHS COMING IN AT NIGHT
Signed, inscribed with title and dated 4/10/19
Pen ink and watercolour with bodycolour
12 ½ x 14 ¼ inches
Redraw of a cartoon that originally appeared in *The Cartoonist*

"The one thing I hate about summer – great big moths coming in at night."

"I'm sorry, sergeant, but I just can't positively identify the man who's been stalking me for the last few weeks."

246 I'M SORRY, SERGEANT, BUT I JUST CAN'T POSITIVELY IDENTIFY THE MAN WHO'S BEEN STALKING ME FOR THE LAST FEW WEEKS
Signed and dated 7/5/19
Pen and ink
7 ¼ × 12 inches
Redraw of a cartoon that originally appeared in *Private Eye*

247 SEAGULL ID PARADE
Signed
Pen and ink with watercolour
8 × 15 ¾ inches
Illustrated: *Private Eye*, September 2019

248 I UNDERSTAND YOUR HUSBAND, A HIGHLY
SKILLED ELECTRONICS ENGINEER, HAS DEVISED
A WAY TO KEEP CATS OFF HIS FLOWER BEDS
Signed and inscribed with title
Pen and ink with watercolour
9 ¾ x 12 inches
Illustrated: *Salisbury Review*, 2019

"I understand your husband, a highly skilled electronics engineer, has devised a way to keep cats off his flower beds."

249 WITH CAREFUL EXCAVATION, I THINK
THESE ANCIENT STONES WOULD TELL
A FASCINATING STORY
Signed and dated 12/9/19
Pen and ink with watercolour
10 ¼ x 20 ½ inches
Redraw of a cartoon that originally appeared in *Private Eye*,
August-September 2019, Page 32

"With careful excavation, I think these ancient stones would tell a fascinating story."

"I REMEMBER HIM WHEN WHEN HE WAS JUST IN MINE DETECTION"

MIKE WILLIAMS
Michael Charles Williams
(born 1940)

Since his first cartoon was published in *Punch* in 1967, Mike Williams has contributed regularly to many a magazine. He has a particular interest in comic representations of animal life, calling this his 'Animalia'.

For a biography of Mike Williams, please refer to *The Illustrators*, 1999, Page 245.

250 I REMEMBER HIM WHEN HE WAS JUST IN MINE DETECTION
Signed and inscribed with title
Pen ink and watercolour
15 x 11 inches
Exhibited: 'The Great Gag Artists of Punch', Chris Beetles Gallery, April 2012, No 135

251 ACHILLES HAS HAD A BLOODY AWFUL SEASON
Signed and inscribed with title
Pen ink and watercolour; 11 x 14 ½ inches
Exhibited: 'The Great Gag Artists of Punch', Chris Beetles Gallery,
April 2012, No 145

252 THEY NEVER FORGET
Signed
Pen ink and watercolour; 11 ¼ x 14 ½ inches

253 MISHAP ON THE STYX
Signed
Pen ink and watercolour; 11 ½ x 14 ½ inches

254 RIGHT LAD, THAT'S TWO GUINNESS, A WHITE WINE,
TWO PACKETS OF SMOKEY BACON CRISPS AND A HEMLOCK
Signed and inscribed with title
Pen ink and watercolour; 11 ½ x 14 ½ inches

PETER BROOKES

Peter Derek Brookes, CBE FRSA RDI
(born 1943)

Peter Brookes maintains the most
consistently high standard of any editorial
cartoonist working in Britain today.
His daily political cartoons and regular
'Nature Notes', produced for *The Times*,
are always inventive, incisive and
confidently drawn. They are the fruit of
wide experience as a cartoonist and
illustrator, and of complete independence
from editorial intrusion.

For a biography of Peter Brookes, please refer
to *The Illustrators*, 2009, page 164.

His work is represented in the collections of
the British Cartoon Archive (University of Kent).

Biteback has recently published Peter Brookes'
latest, long-awaited cartoon collection,
Critical Times.

255 DRAGON'S DEN
Signed and dated '10 iv 19'
Pen ink and watercolour
8 ¼ x 11 ¼ inches
Illustrated: *The Times*, 10 April 2019

256 THERE WILL BE SERIOUS
CONSEQUENCES!
Signed and dated '3 vii 19'
Pen ink and watercolour
8 ¼ x 11 ¼ inches
Illustrated: *The Times*, 3 July 2019

257 CHURCHILLIAN BORIS
Signed and dated '21 vi 19'
Pen ink and watercolour
8 ¼ x 11 ¼ inches
Illustrated: *The Times*, 21 June 2019

258 THE SECOND COMING ...
Signed, inscribed 'After Leonardo's
"Salvator Mundi"' and dated '13 iv 19'
Pen ink and watercolour
8 ¼ x 11 ¼ inches
Illustrated: *The Times*, 13 April 2019

259 NATURE NOTES
ORANGE-UTAN (TRUMPUS RUMPUS)
Signed and dated '6 i 18'
Pen ink and watercolour
8 ¼ x 11 ¼ inches
Illustrated: *The Times*, 6 January 2018

260 NATURE NOTES
SENTIENCE
Signed and dated '25 xi 17'
Pen ink and watercolour
8 ¼ x 11 ¼ inches
Illustrated: *The Times*, 25 November 2017

SIMON DREW
Simon Brooksby Drew (born 1952)

Simon Drew has combined his zoological training, his skill as a draughtsman, and his inventive approach to languages to create a unique and highly popular comic art.

For a biography of Simon Drew, please refer to *The Illustrators*, 2018, Page 157.

As in the last seven years, Simon Drew will produce the 'Spot Puzzle' for the Christmas issue of *The Spectator*.

Nos **261-267** are all designs for Greetings Cards

261 THE ORIGIN OF BIRDS
Signed and inscribed with title
Pen ink and coloured pencil
7 ¼ x 10 ¾ inches

MARY QUEEN OF SPOTS

pet a manger

262 MARY QUEEN OF SPOTS
Signed and inscribed with title
Pen ink and coloured pencil
7 ¼ x 5 ½ inches

263 PET A MANGER
Signed and inscribed with title
Pen ink and coloured pencil
6 ½ x 5 ½ inches

264 DOG BREEDS [I]
Signed and inscribed with title
Pen ink and coloured pencil
7 ¼ x 5 ½ inches

265 DOG BREEDS [II]
Signed and inscribed with title
Pen ink and coloured pencil
7 ¼ x 5 inches

man flu
over the cuckoo's nest

hare, bee 'n bee

266 MAN FLU OVER THE CUCKOO'S NEST
Signed and inscribed with title
Pen ink and coloured pencil
7 ¼ x 5 ½ inches

267 HARE, BEE 'N BEE
Signed and inscribed with title
Pen ink and coloured pencil
7 ½ x 6 inches

MATT

Matthew Pritchett, MBE (born 1964), known as 'Matt'

'His genius lies in being witty without being nasty'

(Charles Moore, quoted in Max Davidson, *Daily Telegraph*, 17 October 2008)

Matt's much-loved pocket cartoons for the *Daily Telegraph* provide a consistently original take on the big news stories of the day.

For a biography of the day, please refer to *The Illustrators*, 2009, page 185.

In addition to the always popular annual, *The Best of Matt*, Orion has recently published *Matt on Brexit*.

Nos **268-277** are all signed, inscribed with title, drawn in pen ink and watercolour, and illustrated in the *Daily Telegraph*

268 WE DON'T WANT A DRONE TO DISRUPT ANY ANGELS WITH TIDINGS
4 x 2 ¾ inches
Illustrated: Sunday 23 December 2018

269 WE'VE LANDED IN THE UK. BRACE YOURSELVES, WE'RE EXPECTING TURBULENCE
3 ¼ x 2 ¼ inches
Illustrated: Wednesday 24 July 2019

270 FUTURE GENERATIONS WILL NOT FORGIVE US IF THEY HAVE TO STUDY THIS IN HISTORY LESSONS
4 x 2 ½ inches
Illustrated: Thursday 21 March 2019

271 YOU NEED TO BRING DOWN YOUR BLOOD PRESSURE. AVOID DOING ANYTHING STRESSFUL, LIKE TRYING TO BOOK A GP APPOINTMENT
4 x 2 ¾ inches
Illustrated: Friday 12 July 2019

272 I'D CALL THAT 'HIGHLY SKILLED'.
IT'S A 'YES' FROM ME
3 ¾ x 3 ¼ inches
Illustrated: Friday 28 June 2019

273 WELL, WE KNOW HE HASN'T
BEEN SEEING ANYONE FROM HMRC
4 x 2 ¾ inches
Illustrated: Friday 11 January 2019

274 YOU KNOW WHAT I MISS?
VOTER APATHY
4 x 2 ½ inches
Illustrated: Sunday 12 May 2019

275 INSTEAD OF PROROGUING
PARLIAMENT, BORIS HAS DIVERTED
HS2 THROUGH HERE
4 ¼ x 3 inches
Illustrated: Wednesday 28 August 2019

276 THAT'S WHEN MPS KNEW HOW
TO BEHAVE. THE BASTARDS WERE
MORE POLITE
4 ¼ x 3 inches
Illustrated: Saturday 28 September 2019

277 FIRST WE BRED A LABRADOODLE,
THEN WE TRIED CROSSING A
REMAINER WITH A LEAVER
4 ¼ x 3 inches
Illustrated: Sunday 29 September 2019

JONATHAN CUSICK
Jonathan Kristofor Cusick (born 1978)

Over the last decade, Jonathan Cusick has gained a strong reputation for his work as an illustrator, and particularly his arresting caricatures, which seem to hold a comically distorting mirror up to personalities who are prominent in the contemporary worlds of politics and entertainment.

For a biography of Jonathan Cusick, please refer to *The Illustrators*, 2010, Page 275.

This year, Jonathan Cusick has produced work for *Radio Times*, notably the Christmas issue, as well as for private clients. The latter includes a Brexit supporter, who commissioned 10 foot banners to stand outside Westminster (and who is now planning to donate them to a museum). He also ran a sell-out drawing workshop at Shrewsbury Cartoon Festival in late April, which he has since repeated.

278 THE QUEEN AND PRESIDENT TRUMP
Signed
Acrylic on canvas
8 x 10 inches
Drawn for the online launch of FattBar

279 WILLY WONKA & THE CHOCOLATE FACTORY
Signed
Acrylic on canvas
16 ¼ x 9 ¼ inches

280 LEWIS HAMILTON
Signed
Acrylic on canvas
13 ½ x 11 inches

281 JOHN BERCOW
Signed
Acrylic on canvas
12 ½ x 9 ½ inches

282 BORIS JOHNSON
Signed
Acrylic on canvas
13 ¾ x 9 inches

SELECT BIBLIOGRAPHY

Backemeyer 2005
Sylvia Backemeyer (ed), *Picture This: The Artist as Illustrator*, London: Herbert Press, 2005

Baker 2002
Martin Baker, *Artists of Radio Times. A Golden Age of British Illustration*, Oxford: The Ashmolean Press & Chris Beetles Ltd, 2002

Bryant 2000
Mark Bryant, *Dictionary of Twentieth-Century British Cartoonists and Caricaturists*, London: Ashgate, 2000

Bryant and Heneage 1994
Mark Bryant and Simon Heneage, *Dictionary of British Cartoonists and Caricaturists 1730-1980*, Aldershot: Scolar Press, 1994

Clark 1998
Alan Clark, *Dictionary of British Comic Artists, Writer and Editors*, London: The British Library, 1998

Driver 1981
David Driver (compiler), *The Art of Radio Times. The First Sixty Years*, London: BBC, 1981

Feaver 1981
William Feaver, *Masters of Caricature. From Hogarth and Gillray to Scarfe and Levine*, London: Weidenfeld and Nicolson, 1981

Horne 1994
Alan Horne, *The Dictionary of 20th Century Book Illustrators*, Woodbridge: Antique Collectors' Club, 1994

Houfe 1996
Simon Houfe, *The Dictionary of British Book Illustrators and Caricaturists 1800-1914*, Woodbridge: Antique Collectors' Club, 1996 (revised edition)

Johnson and Gruetzner
Jane Johnson and Anna Gruetzner, *The Dictionary of British Artists, 1880-1940*, Woodbridge: Antique Collectors' Club, 1986 (reprint)

Khoury 2004
George Khoury (ed), *True Brit. A Celebration of the Great Comic Book Artists of the UK*, Raleigh, NC: TwoMorrows Publishing, 2004

Lewis 1967
John Lewis, *The 20th Century Book*, London: Herbert Press, 1967

Mallalieu 1976
Huon Mallalieu, *The Dictionary of British Watercolour Artists up to 1920*, Woodbridge: Antique Collectors' Club, 1976

Martin 1989
Douglas Martin, *The Telling Line. Essays on fifteen contemporary book illustrators*, London: Julia MacRae Books, 1989

Matthew and Harrison 2004
H C G Matthew and Brian Harrison (eds), *Oxford Dictionary of National Biography*, Oxford University Press, 2004 (61 vols)

Peppin and Mickelthwait 1983
Brigid Peppin and Lucy Mickelthwait, *The Dictionary of British Book Illustrators: The Twentieth Century*, London: John Murray, 1983

Price 1957
R G G Price, *A History of Punch*, London: Collins, 1957

Ray 1976
Gordon Norton Ray, *The Illustrator and the Book in England from 1790 to 1914*, New York: Pierpoint Morgan Library, 1976

Reid 1928
Forrest Reid, *Illustrators of the Sixties*, London: Faber & Gwyer, 1928

Souter 2007
Nick and Tessa Souter, *The Illustration Handbook. A Guide to the World's Greatest Illustrators*, Royston: Eagle Editions, 2007

Spalding 1990
Frances Spalding, *20th Century Painters and Sculptors*, Woodbridge: Antique Collectors' Club, 1990

Spielmann 1895
M H Spielmann, *The History of 'Punch'*, London: Cassell and Company, 1895

Suriano 2000
Gregory R Suriano, *The Pre-Raphaelite Illustrators*, New Castle: Oak Knoll Press/London: The British Library, 2000

Turner 1996
Jane Turner (ed), *The Dictionary of Art*, London: Macmillan, 1996 (34 vols)

Wood 1995
Christopher Wood, *The Dictionary of Victorian Painting*, Woodbridge: Antique Collectors' Club, 1995 (2 vols)

CUMULATIVE INDEX OF CATALOGUES (1991-2018)

INDEX